ALIEN
CONTACT

TALKING POINT

ALIEN CONTACT

Herbie Brennan

Cover illustration by
Mark Thomas

■SCHOLASTIC

Scholastic Children's Books,
Commonwealth House, 1-19 New Oxford Street,
London WC1A 1NU, UK
A division of Scholastic Ltd
London ~ New York ~ Toronto ~ Sydney ~ Auckland

Published in the UK by Scholastic Ltd, 1998
Text copyright © Herbie Brennan, 1998
Cover illustration copyright © Mark Thomas, 1998

ISBN 0 590 19812 2

All rights reserved
Printed by Cox & Wyman Ltd, Reading, Berks.
Typeset by Rapid Reprographics Ltd

10 9 8 7 6 5 4 3 2 1

The right of Herbie Brennan and Mark Thomas to be identified as the author and
artist of this work respectively has been asserted by them in accordance with the
Copyright, Designs and Patents Act, 1988.

CONTENTS

Introduction

Have you ever lain outdoors on a hot summer night and looked up at the stars?

Have you ever wondered if there might be creatures out there, perhaps with hopes and dreams like yours?

Have you ever thought what it might be like to hear the whisper of an alien voice, absorb the wisdom of an alien mind?

It's probably safe to say a majority of astronomers and other scientists now believe there's life out there among the stars.

This conclusion comes from the statistics. There are billions of stars in our galaxy, billions of galaxies in our universe. Some physicists even believe there are billions of universes in our multi-dimensional reality.

The argument is simple. With so many possibilities out there, life *must* have evolved beyond the Earth. With so many possibilities, intelligence *must* have emerged. With so many possibilities, some at least of that intelligence must be greater than our own.

But if a majority of scientists believe that life is out there, it's also probably true to say that most of them are sceptical about the possibility of contact.

Although SETI (Search for Extra-Terrestrial Intelligence) programmes are still in place today, they are generally under-funded and limited in their scope. All of them are based on radio astronomy. If we are ever to hear alien voices, the scientists believe they will come to us coded on the airwaves.

There are, of course, people who believe these scientists are just plain wrong. Flying saucer sightings – whatever flying saucers may be – have now climbed into the millions. There are those who think the saucers come from outer space.

Men, women and some children on every continent claim to have made contact with alien intelligences. In certain cases the contact has been telepathic. In others they say they met aliens face to face.

Some students of religion and mythology have come to the conclusion that the 'gods' of ancient times were not the supernatural beings most of us believe, but astronauts from some unimaginably advanced civilization far beyond our planet.

According to these theories, aliens have visited us in the past and continue to visit us today. People even claim to have recorded alien voices on magnetic tape.

How much, if any, truth is there in these intriguing claims? Is it possible there was once life – or even a great civilization – on the planet Mars? Could a creature like the one in Stephen Spielberg's film *ET* really fly in from the depths of inter-stellar space?

Or is the explanation of UFO and other curious phenomena even weirder? Is it possible we might be visited from alien *dimensions*? Could *time travel* be a reality?

These are just some of the questions posed throughout the remainder of this book. You'll hear the arguments of both the believers and the sceptics. You'll be presented with the information and the evidence.

What conclusions you may reach are up to you.

Can you crack this formula?

$$N = R_* f_p n_e f_l f_i f_c L$$

It has been devised by a leading scientist to represent the number of intelligent civilizations in our galaxy.

Section One

IS ANYBODY OUT THERE?

Professor Frank Drake is President of the SETI Institute. The letters of the acronym stand for Search for Extra-Terrestrial Intelligence.

SETI is a cosmic phone-tap. Astronomers direct the huge dishes of their radio telescopes towards specific segments of the sky, and patient computers monitor every hiss and crackle they pick up. They're looking for a pattern – anything to suggest that a signal from the depths of space might be artificial. They're trying to listen in on ET phoning home.

The first attempt at a SETI (under the name of Project Ozma) dates back to 1958. It was started by Frank Drake, then a newly-qualified astronomer with the recently-created National Radio Astronomy Observatory at Green Bank, West Virginia, in the United States.

Since 1958, Dr Drake's career has taken him to the peak of his profession. He is almost universally accepted as the foremost living authority on extra-terrestrial contact. His opinions carry the full weight of four decades' experience in the field.

In 1991, he went on record with the prediction that the first proven extra-terrestrial contact was no more than nine years away.

In other words, Frank Drake believes we'll hear from ET before the year 2000.

False alarms

➤There have been false alarms.

Early in 1968, the scientific journal *Nature* carried the first news of an astonishing discovery. A team of astronomers at Cambridge Observatory in England had detected a unique stream of radio pulses originating from the deepest reaches of the galaxy. Nothing like it had ever been recorded by radio telescopes before.

Like so many scientific breakthroughs, this one came about by accident. A young research student named Jocelyn Bell was using a radio telescope to gather data for her doctoral thesis. She wasn't searching for extra-terrestrial life. She wasn't even interested in deep space. She was recording interplanetary scintillations – 'sparkles' of radio noise that originate within our solar system.

The telescope she used was fixed – that is, you couldn't turn it to point at any particular segment of the sky. All it did was record whatever happened to pass through its beam. Jocelyn, who was examining just about every signal that passed through its beam, was the first to notice the pattern of activity originating light-years away.

By the time the article appeared in *Nature*, two more unidentifiable radio sources had been found and the entire team of astronomers at Cambridge was monitoring them with barely concealed excitement.

The cause of all the fascination was that the signals they detected *pulsed*. They switched on and off at regular intervals. No known natural phenomenon could account for this. Astronomical objects either emitted steady streams of radiation or they didn't – that was the way the universe worked.

But the pulsed signals were definitely there. One source released a 0.01 second burst of radiation every 1.3 seconds for a period of observation that ran into months. Something had to be turning the signals on and off.

There seemed to be only one possible explanation. The pulses were being created by an extra-terrestrial intelligence.

What Drake found

►Meanwhile, back in the United States, Frank Drake was trying to catch up with his correspondence when his office door burst open and an Australian colleague tossed the *Nature* article on his desk.

Drake was just as excited as his professional counterparts in Cambridge. He desperately wanted to listen to those signals for himself. And he was in luck. The Green Bank observatory schedule permitted him to point the radio telescope directly at the strongest and most well-established source.

Drake did so and found – absolutely nothing.

Making waves

►Radio astronomy is very different from optical astronomy.

Most importantly, optical telescopes are designed to collect visible light. This means that if a star radiates light (and isn't too far away) you can see it. But stars emit much more than light. Some of them generate X-rays. Others produce radio signals.

You can detect visible light simply if it's there to be seen. But radio signals aren't like visible light. If your telescope is tuned to detect them on one wavelength, it will miss them altogether if they happen to be broadcasting on another.

That's what happened to Frank Drake. The sophisticated and expensive American radio telescope at Green Bank was tuned to 430 megahertz. The relatively simple device, which was all that the British could afford, was detecting signals of only 100 megahertz. But that, as it happened, was where the action was originating.

Drake retuned his radio telescope, then reset it to point in the right direction. Immediately he picked up a pulsed signal so strong it jerked the recording pen right off the chart.

This was good, but not good enough. The English equipment was by now detecting at even lower wavelengths. By a spine-tingling coincidence, these were the same wavelengths that carry television pictures on Earth. Was it possible astronomers were listening in on a 24-hour news channel run by aliens from a distant nebula?

Drake was faced with a bizarre problem. His equipment allowed him to go higher than 100 megahertz, but not lower. To listen properly to these strange signals, he needed a new feed to his radio telescope, one that would allow him to tune it downwards.

Normally the procedure to get a new feed was to apply for money from the National Science Foundation or NASA. Drake was far too impatient for that. He walked into the nearest town and used his credit card to buy the largest television aerial he could find. With the help of John Sutton, his Australian colleague, he wired it into the radio telescope mast. This makeshift device worked so well that within weeks the Green Bank observatory had become the world's most important source of information on the new signals from outer space.

Little green men

►*Nature's* story about the mystery signals from outer space soon reached the mass-circulation news media. Reporters swarmed to interview astronomers who, unused to the limelight, were unwary enough to quote to the press the sort of shorthand terms they used among themselves – 'Morse code stars' and even 'LGMs'.

It was that last one that really got the journalists jumping. LGM is another acronym, borrowed from the world of science fiction. The letters stand for 'Little Green Men' and it refers to intelligent extra-terrestrial life forms.

It's probably safe to say that most of the astronomers who talked so glibly about Little Green Men didn't mean it to be taken seriously. It was just a fun label to stick on radio signals nobody understood.

But the press took it seriously. Before the denials started, there was a brief flurry of banner headlines claiming that respected astronomers believed they were receiving Morse code from an alien civilization.

The cosmic lighthouse

►The press claims weren't entirely made up. When the signals were first discovered, almost every astronomer involved wondered whether they had discovered extra-terrestrial life.

But the Cambridge group soon abandoned the idea of extra-terrestrials. They had discovered six different signal sources, light-years apart. Others quickly added ten more to the list. The scientists argued that there were now just too many pulsing sources, spread too widely apart and broadcasting at too many different frequencies for them to be the work of a single extra-terrestrial civilization. And the idea that a different set of aliens was involved in each one stretched the idea beyond belief.

At the time, there was another argument put forward. You'll hear it again, in a different context, later in this book. It is called the 'Limited Energy Hypothesis'. The Limited Energy Hypothesis says simply that however advanced your civilization might be, there's a limit to the energy it can generate. But something in deep space was producing energy in almost unimaginable amounts. With 16 pulsing sources now discovered, the Cambridge scientists were convinced no alien civilization could afford the massive amounts of energy needed to power them.

Frank Drake wasn't so sure. He badly wanted to discover life 'out there' and he still thought the signals might be it. His answer to the Limited Energy Hypothesis was that the power source of the signals might be natural, but was *modified* by aliens to produce the pulsing.

Although it wasn't known at the time, there was another reason to believe Drake might just be right. The signals were *polarized* – that's to say they vibrate on a single plane – exactly like the radio waves broadcast by the BBC.

All the same, the idea that the signals could be the work of intelligent aliens was rapidly losing ground. Even the press was no longer backing it despite its sensational appeal. Astronomers were gradually reaching a consensus that the pulses had some natural origin, even if they hadn't the slightest idea what.

The term scientists used to describe the phenomenon was 'rapidly pulsating radio sources' – a mouthful that made discussion awkward. But Drake and two of his graduate students, Hal Craft and John Comella, coined the term 'pulsar' in a paper they wrote for the journal *Science*. The name stuck. Soon everybody in the scientific community was using it. The trouble was, nobody knew what it really meant.

Then an astronomer named Tom Gold came up with a reasonable explanation. He suggested that the stars sending out the radio signals weren't pulsing at all. Instead they were spinning so rapidly that all their energy was emitted in a single beam that spun around and around like some great cosmic lighthouse giving the *impression* of a pulse.

This theory turned out to be correct in the end, but it contained a real mystery when it was first proposed:

What sort of star could possibly behave in the way Tom Gold suggested?

Neutron stars

➤Our sun shines because it fuses hydrogen in a continuous nuclear explosion that creates light, heat and other forms of radiation. It will continue doing this until its fuel supply runs out.

When this begins to happen, an age-old balance will break down. Gravitational forces once held at bay by the pressures formed in the fusion reaction will force the sun to contract. But this shrinking will raise the temperature again and allow the sun to burn other forms of fuel. It will swell to become a red giant, a huge, comparatively cool star that will swallow the innermost planets of the solar system, including Earth.

At this point the sun will be burning helium. As helium atoms begin to fuse, the star becomes hotter, denser and smaller. When it has exhausted all possible sources of nuclear energy, it will contract further and become what is called a white dwarf, a cold, small husk of its former glory.

But not all stars end up like that. Anything more than three times larger than the sun is too big to support its own weight. At a particular stage of its evolution, such a star begins to collapse in on itself, becoming smaller and smaller, more and more dense. The electrons of each atom are plunged into the nucleus where they fuse with protons to become neutrons. Then the atoms themselves are fused together so the whole star becomes one giant atomic nucleus.

This collapse results in the formation of a neutron star.

Neutron stars are extremely small, high-density stellar corpses composed of tightly packed sub-atomic particles. Just how dense they are is indicated by the fact that in a neutron star, a mass the size of our sun is packed into a sphere only 19 km in diameter. If you made the little ball tip of a ball-point pen from material taken from a neutron star it would contain about 91,000 tonnes of mass. If you could extract enough to fill a teaspoon, it would weigh more than 1,000,000,000 tonnes.

The first astronomer to calculate that certain stars must eventually become neutron stars was the Italian Franco Pacini of the Frascati Observatory near Rome. Just a year before the first pulsar was discovered, he announced that because such stars would be highly magnetic and spin rapidly, they were bound to release enormous quantities of radiation, including radio waves.

Although Pacini said nothing about them pulsing, astronomers began to wonder if Tom Gold's 'cosmic lighthouse' might not be a neutron star.

Scientists at Green Bank and other observatories began to search for a pulsar in the Crab Nebula, which, as the remnant of a supernova (a star that exploded violently), was bound to contain a neutron star. A pulsing star eventually did turn up, but it wasn't at all like the pulsars Jocelyn Bell discovered. Its pulses came every five minutes or so, not every second.

This confusing situation led to a split in astronomical opinion. Some experts still maintained that pulsars pulsed. Others decided to agree with Gold and his lighthouse theory. The problem was, no one could prove it one way or the other. All scientists could do was wait and watch.

What they were waiting and watching for was change. If pulsars really pulsed, they would get denser as they lost their energy and that would make them pulse faster. If they were some sort of spinning lighthouse, the spin would slow down with energy loss and the apparent pulses would become slower and slower. But every pulsar the astronomers observed neither speeded up nor slowed. Every pulsar remained exactly the same.

Except one.

Deep in the heart of the Crab Nebula was the pulsar that didn't behave like any of the others. A graduate student named David Richards discovered that it had a fast, regular pulse like the early pulsars, but every five minutes it abruptly emitted an enormously large pulse. It was this large pulse – roughly a thousand times more powerful than the pulses in between – that had been observed originally at Green Bank. The smaller pulses were missed altogether.

Emboldened by his discovery, Richards closely observed the Crab Nebula pulsar. After nearly a year, he found the pulses were slowing down. They weren't slowing much – just one thirty-sixth billionth of a second a day – but they *were* slowing. The proof was there at last. Pulsars didn't pulse at all: they were cosmic lighthouses, spinning like tops and sending out a tight beam of radiation.

Nobel Prize

►Professor Anthony Hewish was in charge of the Cambridge project at the time when the first pulsar was discovered. He supervised Jocelyn Bell, helped her interpret her findings and was there to assist when she presented them to the press.

In 1974, Professor Hewish was awarded the Nobel Prize for Physics for the pulsar discovery – Jocelyn Bell got nothing.

See for yourself

▶Tonight, when your parents are fast asleep, slip down to the living room and switch on your television set. Turn it to any channel that's closed down for the night so you're staring at a blank screen.

Now wait.

In no more than five minutes you will see a burst of interference, or 'snow' across about one-third of the screen. It won't last long, but if you wait another five minutes, it will happen again.

What you are watching is the radiation from that immense cosmic lighthouse in the Crab Nebula, picked up by your television aerial from a distance of roughly 35,194,176,000,000,000 miles!

SETI today

▶Frank Drake still wanted to believe in extra-terrestrials. Even though the pulsars now had a natural explanation, it was possible something out there might be modifying their radiation to send a signal. He studied the read-outs from pulsar after pulsar. After months of work, he was forced, reluctantly, to conclude he could find no pattern to suggest intelligence might be involved. Pulsar signals were definitely not the work of Little Green Men.

It was a disappointment, but it was not the end of SETI which, despite financial set-backs, has gone from technical strength to strength.

When Drake set up Project Ozma, it took him two months to study the radiation patterns of just two nearby stars. Today that entire project could be completed in a fraction of a second.

In the early days of SETI, the best astronomers could

hope for was that they might examine a few hundred stars over their working lifetime. Today, they can scan for signals from a million stars at once. They can probe distances of a thousand light-years or more.

In 1997, Harvard's Oak Ridge Observatory formally opened BETA, the latest thing in SETI research. BETA stands for Billion-channel Extra-Terrestrial Array. It's a radio telescope that can scan stars for signals on a thousand million frequencies. Obviously, some astronomers still believe there's life beyond this planet.

One of the reasons they still cling to that belief is the Green Bank Formula.

The Green Bank Formula

➤It was the energetic Frank Drake who created the Green Bank Formula. The formula itself looks like this:

$$N = R * f_p n_e f_l f_i f_c L$$

It's a daunting equation the first time you see it. But it's also about the most exciting formula you will ever find. What it sets out to do is calculate the number of technical civilizations that must exist in the Milky Way.

The formula works by combining the factors needed for intelligent life to develop anywhere in the universe. Once you know that, you can start to read it.

The first thing you come across is the letter N. That stands for the **N**umber of technically advanced civilizations out there. Professor Drake says that it is equal to the product of the various factors involved in the evolution of intelligent life.

The first three of these factors are physical.

The letter R stands for the **R**ate at which stars form.

You multiply that by the number of those stars that have planets (expressed as a fraction – f_p, standing for 'fraction with planets') and the average number of planets per star capable of supporting life, symbolized by the value n_e. (What the letters stand for aren't so straightforward from here on. The letter 'n' stands for 'number' as you'd expect, but Professor Drake picked 'e' to stand for 'life', probably to avoid confusion with the use of 'l' a bit later.)

The next two factors are biological.

What you're inserting here is the fraction of those planets where life actually develops (f_l standing for 'fraction with life') followed by the fraction of planets where the life is intelligent (f_i meaning 'fraction with intelligence').

The final two factors are social.

The first of these is the fraction of planets with intelligent life that gets as far as building technical civilizations (f_c standing for 'fraction with civilization'). The second factor is the average lifetime of such civilizations (L = 'lifetime of the civilization').

The values for these various factors are very difficult to fill in. There's good reason to suppose the average rate of star formation in our galaxy is ten, but beyond that guesswork takes over.

Only one planet outside our solar system has ever been detected with certainty – and that only happened in 1996. Wobbles in the orbits of about half our closest stars *may* be made by planets, but even if this was absolutely certain, we have no way of knowing whether it's a general rule throughout the galaxy.

The question of the origin of life is equally uncertain. In 1953, the American biochemist Stanley Lloyd Miller showed that if hydrogen, ammonia, methane and water vapour were subjected to radiation, organic molecules would appear. Organic molecules aren't exactly alive, but are usually produced by biological processes. If you can make them out of chemicals, as Dr Miller did, most scientists agree they might be a first step towards creating life itself.

Later experiments showed that DNA (deoxyribonucleic acid) and RNA (ribonucleic acid), the two molecules which carry the genetic codes that form the basis of life on Earth, could also be produced in this way, another much more promising step forward. Organic molecules have since been discovered floating freely in space, but how they might evolve into life, or whether they were produced by life, is not actually known.

When we come to the question of technical evolution, the problems get worse. The only known example of a technical civilization is our own. How long it took to develop depends on how you define the beginnings of technology. Is it the discovery of fire? The invention of the wheel? The creation of the written word?

When the Green Bank Formula was first invented, scientists put in values for the various factors based on their knowledge at the time. This resulted in their calculating that the number of technical civilizations in our galaxy stood around one – a discovery they might have made by looking through the window.

With time and increased knowledge, more accurate figures have become possible. There is still a great degree of variation and different values obviously produce different results. But the bottom line today places the *minimum* number of technical civilizations in our galaxy at 1,000.

Some scientists think it could run as high as a hundred million.

But the problem is, nobody knows which of these two figures is correct, or whether either is.

No scientist, including Frank Drake, can actually *prove*

there's intelligent life out there, however many formulae they dream up. The best they can do so far is tell you that with so many stars in our universe, an awful lot of planets must have formed. And with all those planets, the chances are at least some of them must have developed life.

It all sounds very vague when you strip away the distracting complications of the Green Bank Formula, but the figures themselves are convincing. There are approximately 1,000,000,000,000 stars in our (Milky Way) galaxy.

And that's not the end of it. Thousands of other galaxies have already been discovered. More are being

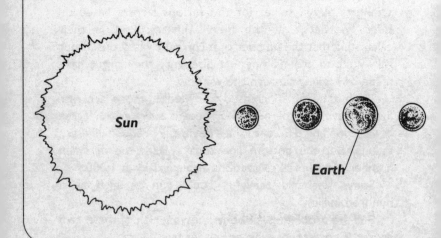

Our solar system is teeming with life, most of it confined to the third planet from the sun.

Sun

Earth

added to the total every day. Astronomers are absolutely certain the total number of galaxies in the universe may well match the number of stars in our galaxy and some think it could far exceed it. The largest galaxy so far charted contains 13 times the number of stars in the Milky Way, but if you were to assume the average number of stars per galaxy was the same as ours, then you have at least 1,000,000,000,000,000,000,000,000 in the universe ... and probably a great many more.

Looking at those figures, you can see why so many scientists believe Earth simply can't be the only home of intelligent life in the entire universe.

But maybe not all of it...

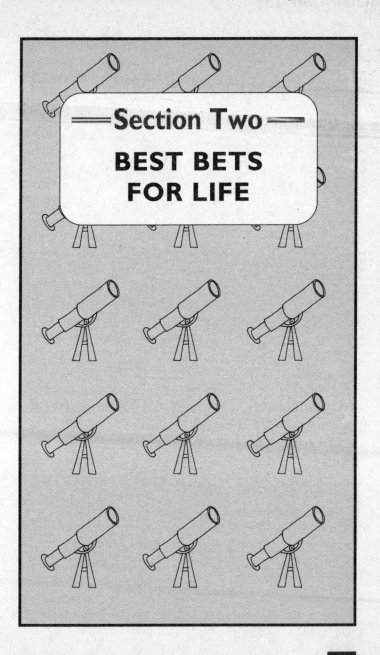

Section Two

BEST BETS
FOR LIFE

There are nine planets in our solar system – in order of distance from the sun, they are Mercury, Venus, Earth, Mars, Jupiter, Saturn, Uranus, Neptune and Pluto.

If you own a good pair of binoculars, you can see eight of them. The one you can't see is Pluto, which is so small and so far away you'd need a powerful telescope.

If you decide to look for them, you can tell the difference between a planet and a star two ways. A star twinkles, but a planet doesn't. Maybe even more importantly, a planet moves while stars stay still. Astronomers in ancient Babylon and Egypt called planets 'wanderers' because of this very fact.

Actually, it's a fact that isn't strictly true. Stars *do* move, many at incredible speeds, but they're so far away you'd be dead before you noticed a change in their position. Planets are a lot closer – about 7,000 times closer than the nearest star – so they seem to change position rapidly.

Apart from Earth, how do the planets look as possibilities for life? Our present spacecraft could just about take you to the furthest reaches of the solar system (so long as you didn't insist on coming back), so let's climb aboard one and inspect the planets one by one.

The winged messenger

➤If you started from the sun, your first port of call would be Mercury. With a diameter of 4,989 km (3,100 miles), Mercury is the second smallest of the planets. It's also nearest to the sun, orbiting roughly 57,934,800 km (36,000,000 miles) away.

(This figure refers to the planet's *average* distance from the sun. None of the planetary orbits are circular, so there are times when they swing closer to the sun and other times when they are further away from it.)

31

In Greek and Roman mythology, Mercury was the messenger of the gods, and pictured as a swift young man with wings on his heels. The description was an accurate one. The planet Mercury moves so fast its year takes only 88 days. This works out at an orbiting speed of 48 km (30 miles) a second.

Mercury is only a little larger than our moon and its gravity is so weak it can't hold much of its atmosphere. Furthermore, while Mercury moves fast in its orbit, it turns very slowly on its axis. Earth takes just 24 hours to complete a single revolution. Mercury takes 1,416 hours, equivalent to 59 days. That doesn't mean a Mercurial day is 59 times longer than our own. Because of its orbit, it's actually 176 times longer. The result is that while night temperatures are a comfortable 21°C (69.8°F), the long, slow day bakes the surface to a massive 427°C, more than enough to vaporize the average carbon-based life form like ourselves. You'd freeze as well. That figure of 21°C (69.8°F) for night temperatures comes from Russian scientists. Western scientists aren't so sure. Some of them calculate that the night side shivers somewhere between -148°C and -180°C (-234°F and -292°F). The coldest region of our own Arctic is practically tropical by comparison at -70°C (-94°F).

Hell in the sky

►Leaving Mercury's orbit, the next planet you reach is Venus. Because of its size, Venus is often referred to as the sister planet of the Earth and it wasn't so long ago that there was serious speculation about life there. The speculation was all the wilder because Venus has a dense white cloud cover that not only makes it the brightest object in the night sky apart from the moon but has also hidden its surface for centuries.

Unfortunately, the clouds have turned out to be composed of sulphuric acid, which has cast a distinct question mark over the possibility of life as you'd quickly discover if you were ever tempted to take a sulphuric acid bath. Within hours, the only part left of you would be your teeth.

There were also signs of water vapour on Venus, which was a little more promising. But as long ago as 1956, radio astronomers at the Naval Research Laboratories in Washington, DC, discovered that the surface temperature of Venus had to be about 315°C (599°F).

American and Russian space probes confirmed this finding and reported back that the surface of Venus was bone dry, whipped by frequent sandstorms and running with volcanic lava that never really cooled down because of the high surface temperature.

Armed with up-to-date information about conditions on Venus, the late astronomer Carl Sagan pointed out that with surface temperatures high enough to melt lead, continual volcanic activity, sandstorms and sulphuric acid rain, it was the closest thing we had in the solar system to the old ideas of Hell.

It struck him as ironic that given the hyper-dense atmosphere, crushing pressure and corrosive conditions, anything living there would need to be squat, with leathery skins and borne up by short, stubby wings – entities very similar to devils. But the suggestion wasn't meant to be taken seriously. Even devils would be hard put to survive under conditions as extreme as those of Venus. Scientists believe no other life form could.

Canals of rock

►Next planet out from Venus is good old Earth, but since you know what's down there, you pilot your ship straight on, heading for the one planet scientists have long thought to be the best bet for extra-terrestrial life – Mars.

As long ago as 1844, French astronomer E.L. Trouvelot observed seasonal brightness changes on its surface and concluded they were due to vegetation. There is a noticeable increase in contrast between bright and dark areas of the planet each spring and some astronomers have reported colour changes as well.

The Italian astronomer, Giovanni Virginio Schiaparelli, was looking at Mars in 1877 when he saw something that made him world famous – a series of thin, dead straight lines crossing the brighter areas of the Martian surface. Further observation of the lines showed they ran for hundreds, sometimes thousands of miles. They also changed with the seasons, exactly like the bright and dark areas observed by Trouvelot.

When Schiaparelli published his findings, he thought the lines were probably channels on the Martian surface. But he published his findings in Italian and when his papers were translated into English, the word for channels (*canali*) was wrongly rendered as 'canals'.

The mistake led to the idea that the 'canals' might have been dug by intelligent beings.

There was scientific controversy not only about this theory, but about the reality of the lines themselves. At one time, it was fashionable to dismiss them as an optical illusion. But when the US spacecraft Mariner IV made a close approach to Mars in July 1965, the pictures it sent back made two things clear.

The first was that the 'canals' were certainly not

artificial. The second was that immense straight-line formations really do exist on Mars (although oddly enough not always in the places where Schiaparelli saw them). Scientists variously explain them as mountains, chains of craters, contour boundaries, fault lines or ridges.

But even without canals, are there any signs of life? The conditions don't look too promising. Temperatures at the equator − 17°C (62°F) − would be pleasant for a human visitor. But general temperatures are very much colder − in the -130 to -30°C (-202 to -22°F) range − and the atmosphere is pure carbon dioxide with a pressure of only six millibars. (Our own atmospheric pressure is over 1,000 millibars at sea level.)

The spacecraft Mariner 4 reported no evidence of water that isn't locked up in the form of ice. Nor is there a magnetic field, which means the Martian surface receives about a hundred times more cosmic radiation than Earth.

Over half of that surface is a desert of reddish rock, sand and soil. The rest of Mars is covered by irregular greenish patches that change through the Martian year. Many astronomers believed them to be some sort of primitive vegetation and a few still do. But the Mariner findings would seem to rule this out. Most scientists now believe the colour changes are chemical, or due to seasonal winds blowing vast quantities of sand across the Martian surface. A few think they're an optical illusion.

There is almost certainly water on Mars, locked up, along with frozen carbon dioxide in the polar ice caps. The ice caps themselves change size with the seasons, but it's the carbon dioxide that's released, not the water.

There are hints (which we'll investigate later) that there may have been life on Mars once. But you'd be hard put to find a respected astronomer who would tell you, hand on heart, there's life on Mars today.

Gassy giant

►Leaving Mars reluctantly behind, you aim your ship at Jupiter, the largest of the planets. It has a diameter of 141,618 km (88,000 miles), 11 times greater than the Earth.

It's a giant ball of gas with no really solid surface. It rotates at a speed of 35,405 km/h (22,000 mph) – the Earth manages just 1,609 km/h (1000 mph) – and takes 12 years to orbit the sun.

The Pioneer 10 and 11 space probes sent back evidence that Jupiter is almost entirely liquid – a combination of hydrogen and helium. Long before a rocky core about the size of the Earth is reached, hydrogen mixed with helium becomes a liquid metal at very high temperature and pressure.

There is absolutely nothing about Jupiter to suggest life in any form could evolve there.

Give me a ring

►If you gaze at the night sky with the naked eye, Saturn is the last of the planets you'll be able to see. It's almost twice as far from the sun as Jupiter – nearly 1,448,000,000 km (900 million miles) – second in size but even less solid.

As you approach in your space ship, you can see that, like Jupiter, it's big – about 71,000 miles at the equator. Its atmosphere is much the same as Jupiter's, as is its structure. It's either all gas, or it has a small dense centre surrounded by a layer of liquid and a deep atmosphere.

Saturn is the one with the rings. This spectacular phenomenon begins about 11,265 km (7,000 miles) above its equator and extends about 56,326 km (35,000 miles) into space. The diameter of the ring system visible from Earth is about 273,581 km (170,000 miles) but the thickness is estimated to be no more than 16 km (10 miles). Radar sightings in 1973 showed the rings were made up of chunks of matter, each averaging a cubic metre in volume.

But there's no one on the surface of Saturn admiring those rings, because, like Jupiter, Saturn has no real surface. It's another gas giant and the chances of its supporting life are close to zero.

It's cold on Uranus!

➤Two hundred years ago, Uranus was called Herschel to commemorate Sir William Herschel, the astronomer who discovered it in 1781. The tradition of naming the planets for classical gods eventually won out, however, and Uranus has been Uranus ever since.

By the time your craft reaches Uranus, the sun has shrunk noticeably behind you. The planet orbits at a distance of 2.9 thousand million km (1.8 thousand million miles) from the sun and has a year 84 times longer than our own. It's four times larger than the Earth and is yet another gas giant. Because of the distance from the sun, it is very, very cold. The chill gives it rather more solidity than, for example, Jupiter since much of its gas is likely to be frozen.

Nobody knows for sure, but the chances are it has a rocky core surrounded by a thick icy mantle. On top of this is a crust of hydrogen and helium that gradually becomes an atmosphere. It will come as no surprise to learn this wholly inhospitable world is not believed to harbour life.

The outer reaches

➤By the time you reach the outer vastness of the solar

system, it's getting seriously cold. It's also getting a shade confusing since the orbits of the last two known planets make it impossible to say definitely which is further from the sun.

Most of the textbooks will tell you Pluto is the last planet you'll find as you leave the system, but until 1999, Neptune actually lies further from the sun. The distance involved is 4.5 thousand million km (2.8 thousand million miles).

Neptune was the last planet visited by the space probe Voyager II before it left our solar system altogether. It's yet another gas giant and has a blue atmosphere with white clouds. Its orbital year is 164 times longer than that of Earth.

Like the other giants, Neptune gives off more energy than it receives from the sun, probably due to an internal heat source. And like the others, the chances of finding life here are non-existent.

Lonely wanderer

➤The last planet you would encounter is Pluto, which *on average* is about 5.7 thousand million km (3.6 thousand million miles) from the sun, but sometimes swings as close as 4.3 thousand million km (2.7 thousand million miles), which is less than the current distance of Neptune. It takes 247.7 years to complete an orbit.

There's frankly not a lot known about Pluto because it's so far away. Astonomers believe its diameter is about 2,300 km (1,430 miles), and its density about twice that of water. Astronomers think it consists of a rocky core surrounded by a thick mantle of ice. Nobody thinks there's life out there.

Life as we know it?

►Three conditions are important when you're considering the possibility of life on other planets: temperature, water and atmosphere. Clearly, these factors relate to carbon-based life forms like ourselves. There may be life, Jim, but not as we know it, on the chill ammonia wastes of Pluto or even in the airless reaches of deep space between the stars. But science cannot speculate on this. It's difficult enough to predict where life like ours might turn up.

Although the three conditions mentioned need not be exactly the same as on Earth, scientists have set the limits beyond which life, as we know it, simply can't exist. These limits are bounded by what they call an *ecosphere*.

The ecosphere for any given star is defined as the (usually small) range of distances from the star where any planets might have temperatures suitable for life, water in liquid form and an atmosphere that does not boil off into space.

The ecosphere of our sun includes the Earth, Moon and Mars.

That last bit of information tells you something very interesting about an ecosphere. Even if a planet falls inside it, that's no guarantee you'll find life there.

The Moon lacks both atmosphere and water. Its temperature range varies between 117°C (242°F) and -190°C (-310°F). Some of the early science-fiction writers described Selenites (Moon people) – but then some of the early science-fiction writers described how you could fly to the moon in a chariot pulled by geese. In reality, the chance of life evolving on the Moon is nil.

Even the brief description you've just read of Mercury and the five outer planets is enough to show there is very little likelihood of their producing life of any sort and none at all of their producing life we would easily recognize.

If there are any other candidates for life in our solar system, they would have to be two of the 16 or more moons of Jupiter and one of Saturn's satellites.

Io, the fifth-closest satellite of Jupiter, is the most volcanically active solid body known. Photographs taken by the Voyager 1 spacecraft in 1979 show a 3,635-km (2,259-mile) diameter moon – about a quarter the size of Earth – that appears yellow, red, brown, black and white. Its surface temperature has been measured at -148°C (-235°F), but a 27°C (80°F) temperature was recorded by Voyager near a volcanic plume. This led to speculation about the possibility of limited organic life, but most scientists don't believe it and no scientist imagines such life could be any more highly evolved than algae.

Europa is Jupiter's fourth largest satellite, discovered by the Italian astronomer Galileo in 1610. It has a diameter of 3,132 km (1,946 miles) and consists mainly of rock with a fairly small component of ice or water. Voyager 1 and 2 photographs show most of the satellite's surface is smooth, bright ice, but there are regions (most of them near the equator) that are darker and mottled.

Europa's most striking feature is a network of lines across the surface. They extend for thousands of miles. These lines are fractures in the ice and since various factors lead astronomers to believe Europa may have a comparatively warm surface, there is just an outside possibility that primitive life may lurk in these huge cracks.

Titan, the largest moon of Saturn, is the only satellite in the solar system known to have clouds and a dense atmosphere. There's a lot of ice on Titan, probably including solid ammonia and methane as well as frozen water. While the surface temperature is a little chilly (about -179°C [-290°F]), that atmosphere is similar in many respects to that of Earth, although lacking oxygen.

Unlike the world it orbits, the surface of Titan is solid enough for life and there is some evidence that its surface features include a vast ocean of liquid methane and ethane. If that evidence is correct, then Titan is a deep-freeze stocked with the types of organic molecules that led to life on Earth four billion years ago. All you need is a little warmth – the result, for example, of volcanic action – and life itself may have developed there.

That life will most likely be microscopic. The very, very best you might hope for on any of these moons would be some very primitive form of vegetation, similar perhaps to earthly lichen. There is no hope of animal life of any sort, certainly no hope of intelligence.

But remember those statistics we were looking at earlier. A million million stars in our little galaxy alone. Anything up to an infinite number of galaxies in the universe. Even though scientists are not at all sure how many of those stars have planets orbiting, some certainly do. And with so many stars, it hardly matters if only one in a million has planets, because you still end up with billions upon billions of planets. Nor does it matter if only one in a million planets is suitable for life. With so many billions of planets, you'll still have millions where life and intelligence is likely to have evolved.

But whatever alien encounters might be waiting in the deep reaches of the galaxy, it looks as if we have no chance of civilized company in our own solar system.

Although there's evidence it may not have always been that way.

You could travel more than 55 million miles in search of life that isn't even as advanced as this patch of lichen.

The question is, would you know it when you found it...?

=Section Three=
THE MARTIANS ARE (MAYBE) COMING!

Two unmanned US spacecraft – Viking I and Viking II – were launched by the National Aeronautics and Space Administration (NASA) on 20 August and 9 September, 1975.

Ten months later, in June 1976, Viking I went into orbit around the planet Mars and began to photograph the surface. The following month, it launched a robot landing craft that touched down at 22° North latitude, 48° West longitude in the region of Chryse Planitia.

When Viking II arrived, a little over a month later, a second landing was made. The site was Utopia Planitia, which lies at 48° North latitude, 226° West longitude.

Both landers set down in these barren rocky wastelands to search for Martian life.

These little spacecraft looked like mechanical insects. Although they cost millions of dollars to build, they stood only a couple of metres high. Each contained a miniature laboratory equipped to carry out experiments designed to detect organic material. If no organic material was present, the craft were programmed to look for any remains that might show organic material had once been there.

Scientists designed the craft so they had various different ways to tackle the problem of finding Martian life. The first was to look around.

Phase One

➤Almost as soon as the landers had touched down, periscopic cameras emerged and began to rotate in a full circle taking both visible light and infra-red pictures of the immediate surroundings. As they did so, broadcast images of the pictures were beamed back to Mission Control on Earth.

The thinking behind this approach was so basic it's

47

almost funny. Scientists wanted to find out if close range pictures would show up maybe a tuft of Martian grass, a skeetering Martian lizard, the remains of some tumble-down Martian shack or the fossil of a Martian dinosaur.

Nobody really expected any of these things, but as a scientist you have to check out every possibility. In the event, nobody was disappointed. The cameras picked up not a single sign of life, past or present.

Phase Two

►With the obvious approach ruled out, the project moved into its second phase. This involved a direct chemical analysis of the Martian soil around the landers.

What the scientists were looking for in this analysis was any indication of organic compounds. Such compounds wouldn't absolutely prove the presence of life, but they would certainly make it likely.

The analysis was extremely sensitive. It reported not a trace of any organic compound.

Phase Three

►The search now moved into its third phase. The labs inside the landers were designed to look for three particular processes typical of life. The processes were metabolism, respiration and photosynthesis.

Metabolism is the name scientists give to the chemical reactions used by the cells of your body to generate energy, stay healthy and produce new cells. You're not the only one whose cells work this way. Every known life form, from single-celled algae to blue whales, depend absolutely on metabolism to keep them going. If you can spot the process of metabolism, the chances are you've spotted life.

The term respiration, as used by scientists, actually covers two different processes. The first one is breathing, which goes beyond the familiar use of your lungs to include any means used by a living organism to take in oxygen and push out carbon dioxide. (Under this definition, fish breathe.)

The second process covered by the term respiration is the release of energy inside living cells from molecules of carbohydrates and fats. It's your cellular version of eating, digesting, then using the energy you create to play a game of basketball. Carbon dioxide and water result from this process which works much the same way from an amoeba to an elephant.

Photosynthesis is usually associated with plants, although some bacteria use it as well. If you're a plant with chlorophyll (which is more or less every plant you've ever seen since chlorophyll is what makes them green), then photosynthesis is the way you catch light and turn it into chemical energy.

From one point of view, every life form on Earth depends on photosynthesis for its survival. If you're a plant, you eat sunlight. If you're an animal, you eat plants or other animals (which eat plants), so wherever you are in the food chain, you're really eating sunlight in one form or another.

Scooping and sampling

➤To search out the process of photosynthesis, or even chemosynthesis, which is the same sort of process except it doesn't involve light, a lander first scooped up several Martian soil samples. The scoop, like the lander itself, was as sterile as NASA could make it. The last thing anybody wanted was to discover a host of 'Martian' bacteria that would turn out to have been exported from Earth.

In the first experiment (called the Pyrolitic Release

experiment), a Martian soil sample was placed inside a chamber filled with Martian air drawn from outside the lander and carbon dioxide containing trace elements of radioactive carbon-14 was injected into the chamber.

For five days the experiment was left alone, then the soil sample was gently heated until it gave off vapour.

The whole idea was that if there were any vegetable organisms in the Martian soil, they would breathe in the carbon dioxide that had been injected into the chamber. In doing so, they would also have taken in the carbon-14. This radioactive element would then be detected at the end of the experiment.

The end result was that if the radiation detector picked up only background radiation, you had to say there was no sign of life. But if there was any radiation higher than back-ground, it would be a strong indication that life was present in the soil.

The background level of radiation was 15. The experiment produced a radiation reading of 96. No known inert chemical process could account for this result.

All the same, a control version of the same experiment was carried out. A new soil sample was heat-sterilized prior to repeating the same steps as before. In yet another control, the xenon lamp (that produced artificial sunlight) was turned off. Both times, the radiation remained at background.

This too pointed to the presence of life. Most plants die off when baked and need light to synthesize energy.

The scientists decided to make trebly sure. They heated the soil sample again, but only to 32°C (90°F). This is a temperature well within the survival range of most plants we know on Earth, so you would expect that if life was really present, the positive results of the first experiment would be repeated.

They were.

Gas exchange

➤The second experiment was called the Gas Exchange Experiment. In it another soil sample was placed in a chamber. The sample was exposed to a damp atmosphere, then treated with a variety of organic nutrients.

The theory behind this one was that if there was any life in the soil, microbes would eat the nutrients and give off gas. The release of gas would change the balance of the atmosphere inside the sealed chamber. Certainly this is what would happen with fertile soil on Earth.

It was also what happened on Mars. Large quantities of oxygen were released as soon as the nutrients were added.

This seemed too good to be true, so the scientists controlling the robots decided to bake the soil sample and see what happened. They cooked it at a temperature of 145°C (293°F) for three hours. That's enough to kill off any known terrestrial bacteria. It made no difference on Mars. When more nutrient was added, more oxygen was given off. If you'd decided your first result was due to life, this result was unexpected. The scientists didn't quite know what to make of it.

Gas release

➤In the third experiment (called the Labelled Release Experiment) the soil sample was covered with a nutrient that contained radioactive carbon-14. The idea was that if there were any microbes in the soil they'd eat the nutrient and give off carbon-14 gas. Unlike the previous experiment, this would show beyond any doubt that something was converting the nutrient directly. Without the carbon-14 test, there was just the outside possibility that the oxygen release was due to some sort of chemical reaction.

Large amounts of carbon-14 gas were given off.

Since the scientists were worried by the result of the previous experiment, they baked this sample too. The release of gas promptly stopped, exactly as it should have done if the gas was caused by bacteria. Even on its own, this set of results would have been accepted as incontrovertible proof of biological action had the experiment been carried out on Earth.

The cautious scientists went for another variation of the test. Here the sample was heated to the relatively low temperature of 50°C (122°F). The results were astounding. Carbon dioxide within the soil started to be released and reabsorbed on a cycle that corresponded to the length of the Martian day.

Chemical reactions are not known to be cyclical. Only life adapts to the changes between day and night.

An odd conclusion

➤The scientists in charge of the project on Mars decided no life signs were present.

This view was not widely challenged. The only real controversy centred on the fact that the experiments were carried out at just two sites and thus were limited in their scope.

A dissenting voice

➤The scientist who designed the Labelled Release Experiment was Dr Gil Levin. He was one of the few who firmly believed the Viking lander experiments pointed to the presence of life.

He set out to prove it by testing life-bearing rocks from Antarctica. His findings removed every scientific objection to the Martian results.

He published his findings. They were ignored or dismissed by his colleagues. One claimed his work was trivial. Another insisted he had misinterpreted the Viking lander data.

The case against life

►The scientist who designed the Pyrolitic Release Experiment was Dr Norman Horowitz. He started out as a believer that there was (microscopic) life on Mars. But his illusions were shattered (his own words) when he saw the dead craters in the photographs sent back by Mariner 4.

Before the Viking landings, he went on record with the evaluation that the chances of finding life on Mars were a 'flat zero'. He believed many of those who disagreed with him were suffering from wishful thinking.

In his book *To Utopia and Back: The Search for Life in the Solar System*, he put the case against Martian life in these words:

Viking found no life on Mars, and, just as important, it found why there can be no life. Mars lacks that extraordinary feature that dominates the environment of our own planet, oceans of liquid water in full view of the sun; indeed, it is devoid of any liquid water whatsoever. It is also suffused with short-wavelength ultraviolet radiation. Each of these circumstances alone would probably suffice to ensure its sterility, but in combination they have led to the development of a highly oxidizing surface environment that is incompatible with the existence of organic molecules on the planet. Mars is not only devoid of life, but of organic matter as well.

A NASA conference – and a confrontation

►In 1986, NASA sponsored a reunion conference for former Viking team scientists. Levin and Horowitz both attended.

Dr Levin gave a slide presentation, in which he not only restated why he thought the Viking test results indicated life, but also suggested seasonal colour changes might indicate vegetation.

Dr Horowitz confronted him afterward and Dr Levin claims they almost had a fist fight.

The Moscow experiment

►In 1980, four years after NASA concluded there were no signs of life on Mars, an interesting but little-publicized experiment was carried out at the Space Biology Laboratory of Moscow University.

Russian scientists set up a sealed tank inside which they built a sort of miniature Mars. They used the information sent back by the Voyager landers to create the exact mix of gases in the Martian atmosphere. They made sure that radiation levels inside the tank were identical to those on the surface of Mars. In so far as it was possible, they made sure that anything entering the tank would experience the precise conditions they would encounter on the surface of the Red Planet.

When the tank was ready, they introduced a variety of terrestrial life forms.

As you might imagine, birds and animals died within seconds. But when they tried introducing reptiles, some lizards survived for hours. Insects did even better. Many were still alive after weeks. It was beginning to look as if the Martian environment wasn't nearly so hostile to life as everyone believed.

When it came to vegetation, it wasn't hostile at all. The shock result of the experiment was that when fungi, algae, lichens, mosses, beans and cereals like oats or rye were introduced, they not only survived, but, given time to acclimatize, actually thrived.

Signs of life

➤Twenty-one years after deciding the results of the Viking lander experiments didn't indicate past or present life on Mars, NASA changed its mind.

The timing couldn't have been better. On 6 August 1996, Hollywood launched its latest science-fiction blockbuster, a thriller called *Independence Day*, all about an alien invasion of Earth.

As patrons filed into the cinema for the world première, the news broke that NASA scientists had discovered evidence of life on Mars.

A few people thought it might be a promotion for the movie, but in the end, this was no silly season story. The announcement was official.

Visitors from space

➤If you watch the night sky long enough, the time will come when you're rewarded by the sight of a shooting star. Make a wish, then consult your nearest astronomer who'll tell you a shooting star isn't a star at all, but a meteor.

In astronomy, a meteor is a small solid body that enters Earth's atmosphere from space. It shines because it's moving so fast it starts to burn up through friction with the atmosphere. Large meteors turn into fireballs with a luminous head and tail you may be able to see for several minutes. A few explode – this type is called a bolide. If they're close enough you can hear the sound, which is rather like distant thunder.

It's the smaller, fainter meteors that are called shooting stars.

When it isn't making movies about alien invasions, Hollywood sometimes makes movies about meteorites that collide with the Earth and do more damage to New York than King Kong. But movies aside, most meteors burn up completely in flight and fall to Earth as dust. The few that don't, the few that actually get right down to the surface, are called meteorites.

Scientists divide meteorites into three major types – irons, stones and stony irons.

Irons, sensibly enough, are made up mainly of iron, with a small percentage of nickel, and traces of other metals like cobalt. Stones consist of silicates, the largest class of minerals. Stony irons are a mixture of iron and stone.

There *are* some big ones and these strike the Earth with enormous impact. The biggest we know about fell in Namibia, in Africa, and weighed about 55 tonnes. The next biggest, weighing more than 31 tonnes, came down in Greenland and has long been used by the Inuit people as a source of metal for their knives.

Big or small, most meteorites are bits of asteroids or comets, but not all. A few are fragments of the *moon*, a few are fragments of the planet Mars. Astronomers believe they broke off from these bodies due to asteroid impact millions of years ago and travelled through space for aeons until captured by the Earth's gravity.

Unless somebody happens to be watching, it's difficult to spot where a small meteorite falls to Earth. It may do a bit of damage at the time, but given a few years of weathering, it starts to look like all the other rocks around it, or it gets covered over with vegetation. If you're hunting for meteorites, it makes sense to look somewhere without vegetation where there aren't too many other rocks about.

The Americans have been meteorite hunting for years in a place like this – the vast, frozen wasteland of Antarctica.

The Martian meteorite

►Some 12,000-13,000 years ago a smallish meteorite crashed into the Allen Hills area of Antarctica. US scientists found it during routine investigations in 1984.

On the surface it looked much like any other meteorite – rocky, pitted, unimpressive. But examination by scientists from NASA, the UK's Open University and Natural History Museum soon showed the rock contained glass bubbles full of gas. When they analysed the gas, they found it to be exactly the same composition as the Martian atmosphere. There was only one possible conclusion – the meteorite came from Mars. The scientists presumed it had 'splashed off' the Martian surface under the force of some sort of impact.

Although it landed around the end of the Ice Age, the Martian rock was estimated to be four and a half *thousand million* years old – much older than any meteorite previously discovered. The experts think it was part of the original crust when the planet was first formed.

This was not the first Martian meteorite to be found in Antarctica, but it soon turned out to be the most exciting. Inside the meteorite were chalky structures that contained what seemed to be the fossil signatures of very primitive microscopic life forms.

Mars is a cold, dry, barren place today, but work by Dr Monica Grady of the Natural History Museum indicates this was not always so. At the time the fossil bacteria were alive, the Martian climate was hot and wet. Consequently life was much more likely to evolve.

But had life, primitive microscopic life, actually evolved? NASA scientists were certain of it and their claims made headlines around the world.

Predictably, not everyone agreed. One group of scientists decided that the 'fossils' were actually geological accidents. Another said they were organic, but came from Earth, not Mars, and had contaminated the meteorite as it lay in Antarctica. There were even suggestions NASA had blown the evidence out of all proportion in order to get higher government grants.

NASA stuck to its guns and the controversy looks set to rage.

This seems to be a sculpture of a human face.

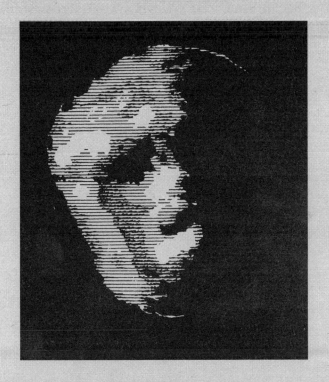

So what's it doing on the planet Mars?

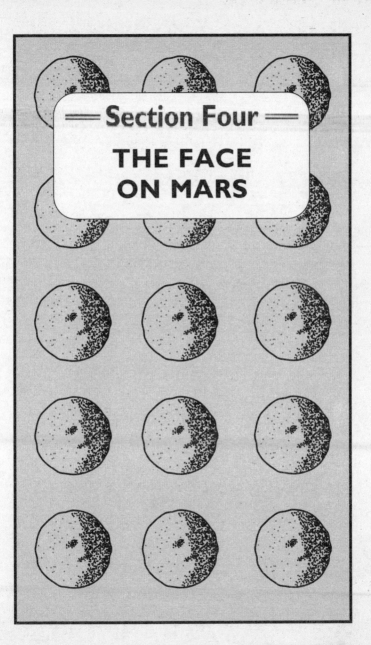

Section Four

THE FACE
ON MARS

In 1987, nearly a decade before announcing the news of microscopic Martian fossils, NASA released photographs of other Martian 'meteorites' found in the Antarctic.

One of them looked for all the world as if four stone blocks had been shaped by a mason and joined together.

It seemed to be a section of a wall.

The Viking probes – a strange discovery

►Eleven years earlier, in June 1976, the unmanned Viking I, a NASA space probe, went into orbit around the planet Mars. Just under two months later, it was joined by Viking II. The two craft took some sixty thousand photographs of the Martian surface.

Five of them showed a rock formation that looked like a human face.

Three years after the pictures were returned, independent experts began seriously to analyse the NASA images of the Cydonia region where the face had turned up. They were interested not only in this curious formation but in several other nearby features of an unusual nature.

In 1993, a group of highly respected academics from the United States and Sweden endorsed a report by Professor Stanley V. McDaniel on the Martian anomalies.

The report presented evidence that the 'face' was artificial.

The face in space

►As the foremost living expert on extra-terrestrial intelligence, Dr Frank Drake was asked his opinion of the face. He thought it was 'just an accident of topography and photography' like the 'Man in the Moon'.

NASA held much the same view back in the Seventies. Official statements described the Face as a trick of light and shade created by the way sunlight struck a natural rock formation.

The two best Viking images of the Face were taken at different angles of the sun (10° and 27°). They were also taken with different camera angles, satellite altitude and orbital inclination. Professor McDaniel argues that if the Face really was a trick of the light, you shouldn't be able to see it at all when the light changed. Other experts agree.

Shape and shade

►Photoclinometry is a scientific technique that estimates the shape of an object from the different tones in a photograph. It extracts the shape from the shading.

Dr Mark Carlotto applied the technique to the Viking photographs. With it, he worked out a three-dimensional structure from each of the two main images of the Face. Both structures were identical. He was also able to *predict* what one image would look like at a different sun angle by analysing the other. He concluded that what seems to be a face in the photographs was actually a face on the ground, not a trick of the light and not an illusion like the 'Man in the Moon'.

Old Man of the Mountain

►Not everybody was impressed by Dr Carlotto's discovery. Critics simply said that even if there really was a rock formation on Mars that looked like a face, this didn't mean the formation was artificial. They point to the fact that there's a natural rock formation in New Hampshire, USA, that looks so much like a face it's been christened

The Old Man of the Mountain. To them, the Face on Mars is a freak carved out by natural wind erosion.

But Professor McDaniel doesn't accept this view. He points out that the Old Man of the Mountain has human features *in profile*. The face on Mars is seen head-on and, if you accept Dr Carlotto's findings, is fully three-dimensional. This is a far more complicated structure for nature to mimic than a simple profile. In fact, says the good Professor, there isn't a single known example of a natural three-dimensional formation like it anywhere on Earth, the Moon or even Mars if we ignore the Face itself.

What's in a face?

►How much like a face is the Martian rock formation? The first published photographs showed the outline of a nose, an eye socket and a portion of a mouth framed by some sort of platform that looked like a helmet. The rest of the face – if there really was any more of it – was in shadow.

But it turned out that wasn't all there was to it. Cameras on spacecraft don't work like ordinary cameras. That's to say, they don't use plates or film sensitized by silver nitrate that reacts to light. Instead, on-board computers *digitize* the image the cameras see and transmit the code back to base. When it arrives, computers at Mission Control translate the data back into a visual image.

The first translation produces a broad image of what the camera saw; and this is what NASA published. If you want to see the fine detail, you have to use a process called computer enhancement.

Computer enhancement isn't like retouching and it isn't guesswork either. The computer starts a rigorous mathematical analysis to recover the information that went into every individual pixel of the original. When you get back pictures from space, your next step after examining the broad basic image is to use computer enhancement. It's standard procedure.

Computer enhancement of the Face on Mars shows there are teeth in the mouth, a brow over the eye and an eyelid and a raised pupil within it. The helmet-like platform surrounding the whole structure is decorated with evenly spaced diagonal stripes. There is a crescent diadem on the forehead made from crossed lines at the exact axis of symmetry. This headpiece continues round into the shadow side of the face to frame the head. The line of the mouth also continues. There is a second eye socket just where you'd expect it to be.

The artist and anthropologist James Channon examined the Face and discovered it has the classical proportions he had learned at art school.

Erosion or aliens?

►These details cast a huge question mark over the idea of wind erosion. Each one would have to be explained by a different geological process in a natural formation. The odds against all these different factors coming together to produce something recognizable as a face would be enormous.

There is another reason to believe wind erosion did not produce the Face. Geologist James L. Erjavec created an extensive feature map of the Cydonia region. In a 1996 scientific paper, he pointed out that the wind erosion theory of formation was based on the idea that the northern lowland plains of Mars were once covered by a kilometre or more of sediment.

But in 1989, another geologist, G. E. McGill, showed conclusively that no more than 200 metres of material could have been stripped off the plains. This isn't enough to produce the Face.

Fractal weirdness

►Fractals are peculiar geometric figures in which any given area is a small copy of a larger portion. Fractal analysis is based on the discovery that natural landscapes follow the rules of fractal mathematics, but man-made things don't. If you run a fractal analysis of a natural object and graph the results, the graph is a straight line. Do the same for an artificial construction of any sort and the graph is curved.

What this comes down to is that if you run a fractal analysis of something you're not sure of, the more curved the graph, the more likely the thing is to be artificial. The technique is used a lot by the American military on satellite photographs. They've found it to be 80% accurate.

Fractal analysis was applied to the Face on Mars by Dr Carlotto and his colleague Michael C. Stein. It gave them much the same curve you'd find on the fractal analysis of a London bus.

Pyramid weirdness

►The Face is situated at Cydonia Mensae, a region of buttes and mesas along an escarpment separating heavily cratered southern highlands from the lowland plains to the north of Mars. Cydonia Mensae has a number of other structures unlike anything seen elsewhere on the planet. Several of them seem to be pyramids.

One of them, known as the D&M Pyramid, is five-sided and symmetrical apart from what appears to be impact damage on its eastern side. In 1988, the geographer and cartographer Erol Toron tried to find out what natural process could produce a shape like this. As a scientist, he knew there were only five possibilities:

1. Water, or some other liquid, shaping the natural rock.

2. Volcanic action sending up lava that solidifies in a particular shape.

3. Sand particles carried by strong winds which gradually 'sandpaper' the landscape into shape.

4. The force of gravity acting on natural substances to distort them into a particular shape.

5. Crystal growth.

Apart from crystal growth, which seemed highly unlikely right from the beginning, Toron considered each of these possibilities well worth a look. There is clear evidence that Mars once had rivers, so water may have shaped the rock. Although a quiet planet now, it once had extensive volcanic activity as well. It certainly has strong winds and sand, even to this day. And while smaller than the Earth, Martian gravity is still a factor in shaping the features on its surface.

But all these various factors – including crystal growth – follow known laws of physics so it's possible to find out which were involved. Toron's analysis ruled out each of them in turn. Since he was very wary of the theory that the pyramid might be artificial, he concluded that 'no known mechanism of natural formation could yield a satisfactory account of the observed general characteristics of the object'. In other words, if it was natural, it broke all the known laws of physics.

Dr Carlotto had no such hesitation. He ran a full fractal

analysis of the area and found three pyramids generated the curved graph that showed they were artificial constructions. This conclusion was backed by a four-year study (published in 1993) by the award-winning architect Robert Fiertek, who used NASA photographs to measure the distances and alignments between the various odd things present in the Cydonia region. His bottom-line conclusion was that:

> *It can be argued that individual objects at Cydonia may or may not be artificial, but it is very doubtful that the complex as a whole is anything but artificial.*[1]

The ultimate weirdness

➤Perhaps the best-known lecturer and writer on the Martian Face is Richard C. Hoagland, winner of the Angstrom Foundation's First International Angstrom Medal for Excellence in Science for his work on hyper-dimensional physics.

Hoagland made extensive measurements of all the structures at Cydonia and found much of the complex was laid out in accordance with the principles of sacred geometry.

Sacred geometry is the name scholars use for a complex tradition of relationships that influenced the temple architecture of Ancient Greece and Egypt.

But the Face on Mars is approx. 2.5 km long by 2 km wide and 42 km high. The D&M Pyramid 13.6 km to the south-west is 2.6 km long by 1.7 km wide by 0.6 km high. If these structures are artificial, they make the temples of Ancient Greece and Egypt look like children's toys.

New probes on the way

➤Following the discovery of what seemed to be microscopic Martian fossils, NASA launched some further unmanned probes towards the Red Planet, as did the Russians.

It was the beginning of a whole new programme designed to settle once and for all the question of Martian life. The first phase of this programme was the landing, on Friday 4 July 1997, of the Pathfinder spacecraft on the Red Planet.

When it was coming down, Pathfinder looked a lot like the Michelin Man. NASA scientists had come up with the ingenious idea of enclosing the craft in airbags that automatically inflated a certain distance from the Martian surface. The idea was that although it might come down a little fast, the airbags would protect the sensitive instruments inside, just as they protect humans in a car crash.

Although there were some doubts about the idea, it worked perfectly. Pathfinder landed and bounced, then landed and bounced again. Eventually it ran out of bounce and stopped. The airbags deflated and out trundled Sojourner — a little robot-controlled vehicle designed to send back close-up pictures of Martian rocks and anything else it might find. At least that was the theory. The reality was that Sojourner got caught up in one of the deflated airbags and couldn't move.

For two anxious days, Mission Control sent signals in the hope of freeing their little robot and on 6 July eventually succeeded. Sojourner trundled off and soon NASA was receiving the first close-ups of the Martian surface for 21 years. Mission Control lost contact with Pathfinder on 2 September. By then, the little Sojourner robot had crawled around a lot of rocks without finding evidence of life. But as the programme proceeds and further probes arrive somewhere in the year 2000, one of the areas they will investigate is Cydonia. The hope is that new photographs might – just might – solve the problem of the strange structures there.

In the meantime, the scientific controversy around them continues to heat up. And for good reason.

If the Face on Mars really is artificial, it overturns what we believe to be the history of the human race.

The Face – what it means

➤ Assume the Face is artificial.

We know it wasn't carved by human beings. Our technology is only just advanced enough to send an astronaut to Mars[2], not mount a major engineering scheme.

If scientists are right when they claim inter-stellar travel is impossible – a point we'll be examining in the next chapter – then it can't have been carved by aliens from beyond the solar system.

Which only leaves one possibility – it was carved by native Martians.

Now that NASA scientists have found evidence of microscopic fossil life, the idea of native Martians isn't quite as daft as it was once thought to be.

But it isn't enough for us to say there once were native Martians with the engineering skills to build the giant structures at Cydonia, fantastic though that may be in itself. The problem is the Face they carved is definitely human.

We've already seen that the chances against two identical species evolving simultaneously on neighbouring planets are literally astronomical. So in order to become familiar with a human face, Martians must once have visited the Earth.

Is such a visit even possible?

Martian evolution

➤ The oldest fossils found on Earth are 3,465 million years old, discovered in a layer of chert from Western Australia. They are the remains of microscopic bacteria quite similar to those NASA found in the Martian rock.

But the Martian life forms are dated to 3,600 million years ago, more than 100 million years earlier.

This suggests the evolution of life on Mars had a 100 million year head start on the evolution of life on Earth. If the pace of evolution on both planets was much the same, intelligence would have appeared on Mars 100 million years earlier than it did on Earth. It is also true to say civilization would have appeared on Mars 100 million years earlier than it did on Earth.

This means our present level of technology would have been reached by Martians 100 million years ago. In the days when dinosaurs roamed the Earth, the Martians could have been planning space flights.

The ancient eras of Earth

➤ The prehistory of Earth is divided into three eras. One of these, the Mesozoic, comprises the three great periods of the dinosaurs — Triassic (245 to 208 million BP), Jurassic (208 to 144 million BP), and Cretaceous (144 to 66.4 million BP).

If Martians were 100 million years ahead of us in evolution, they would have turned their minds to space flight sometime during Earth's Cretaceous period.

Martian journey into space

►It's interesting to realize that, for a Martian, space flight would have been a much easier technical problem to solve than it has been for terrestrial humanity.

The reason for this lies in the physical characteristics of the two planets. Mars has a mass of just over one-tenth that of Earth. Its surface gravity at the equator is just 3.72 cm per second squared as opposed to 9.78 here. This is the factor that influences what's called escape velocity. Escape velocity – the speed you need before you can leave a planet – is 11.2 km per second on Earth. It's only 5 km per second on Mars.

In other words, you only need to travel about half as fast to get off Mars than you do to get off Earth. This has knock-on implications. Lower escape velocity means less fuel and a less efficient engine will get you into space.

Although it's obviously easier to get into space if you're a Martian, the question arises whether Martians were likely to want to. Obviously nobody can be sure about this, but psychologists claim the presence of the Moon played an important part in turning human minds towards space flight. Put simply, we looked up, saw it, and wondered how to get there.

Mars has two moons, Phobos and Deimos. Both are visible from the planetary surface. Both are much closer to Mars than our Moon is to Earth. Our Moon orbits some 384,400 km away. Deimos is only 23,460 km from Mars. Phobos is even closer – just 9,380 km.

The first logical goal in any space programme is to orbit the planet. The second is to reach the nearest astronomical body. Our nearest astronomical body is the Moon, which we reached in July 1969. Compared to that trip, reaching little nearby Phobos would have been a piece of cake for the ancient Martians.

Once you reach your satellite, you naturally turn your attention to your planetary neighbours. Mars has two – Earth and Jupiter. At its closest approach, Earth is less than 56 million km from Mars. The closest Jupiter gets is more than 491 million km.

But even if Jupiter were closer, it's unlikely that Martians would have been interested in, or even capable of, a visit. Their astronomers would have alerted them to the crushing gravity more than 600 times what they were used to at home. Their spacecraft would need almost eleven times Martian escape velocity to get off again, even if – somehow – it managed to make a safe landing.

But they couldn't have made a safe landing. As we've already seen, Jupiter is a giant made of gas. It lacks the slightest possibility of a landing site. If Martians headed anywhere, it would have been Earth.

Read this Biblical quotation carefully...

And it came to pass when men began to multiply
on the face of the earth and daughters were born
unto them, that the sons of God saw the
daughters of men that they were fair; and they
took them wives of all which they chose.

Genesis VI: verses 1 and 2.

**Some people think it's our earliest record of
extra-terrestrial contact.**

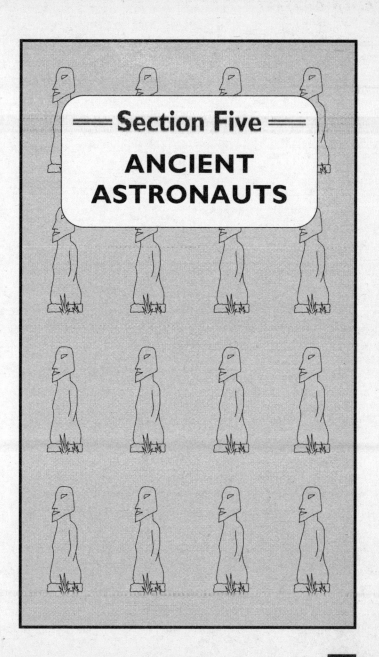

Section Five

ANCIENT ASTRONAUTS

NASA scientists went no further than their claim that there was once microscopic life on Mars. Astronomers speculate there might – just might – be microscopic life on Io, Titan or Europa. But the Green Bank Formula suggests there are up to a hundred million technical civilizations elsewhere in our galaxy.

In 1968 a Swiss author put forward the theory that not only is advanced intelligence 'out there', but it has already visited planet Earth.

Erich von Daniken

►Erich von Daniken was born in Switzerland in 1935. At the age of 19 he seems to have had some sort of vision. Later he spent a good deal of his time in meditation and experienced periods of *déjà vu*, that curious feeling of having lived through a particular experience before.

He also started to write. When the guests went to bed, hotel manager von Daniken often pounded his typewriter until four in the morning.

The book he was writing was called *Memories of the Future*. In 1967 the manuscript was accepted by the Swiss publisher Econ-Verlag. In March the following year Econ-Verlag issued a smallish edition of 6,000 copies.

Nobody knew it at the time, but a juggernaut was starting to roll.

The flying chariot

►In the week von Daniken's book was published, a Swiss newspaper began to run it in serial form. The publicity meant Econ-Verlag quickly sold out of their first edition and had to print a second, then a third.

Von Daniken's book was written in German and

became the No. I bestseller in Germany by the end of 1968. In 1969, the first English language translation appeared in London. A Bantam Books edition in the United States sold more than a quarter of a million copies in two days.

The book wasn't called *Memories of the Future* any more. The English-language editions went out under the title *Chariots of the Gods?*

Arrival of the space gods

►What excited everybody so much about the book was von Daniken's theory that the 'gods' of ancient times and even God Himself, as described in the Old Testament, were actually visitors from outer space. Faced with their spaceships and advanced technology, primitive humanity believed them to be supernatural beings.

Von Daniken went further. In his own words:

I ... proclaim that these 'strangers' (the extra-terrestrial visitors) annihilated part of mankind existing at the time and produced a new, perhaps the first, Homo sapiens.[3]

This was a mind-blowing idea, but not entirely crazy. As the movie version of his book went into particular detail to point out, we already had something similar happening in more recent times with cargo cults.

Cargo cults

►The aboriginal peoples of Melanesia and New Guinea were first exposed to European contact in the nineteenth century. The impact on their ancient tribal culture was devastating. Old ways were abandoned and the idea arose that the purpose of life was to possess trade goods – cargo – like the Europeans.

Very quickly, cargo took on a religious significance.

The situation worsened with the outbreak of the Second World War when the area was flooded with troops bringing with them their high-tech transport vehicles, flying machines and frequent landings of cargo.

In the eyes of the aboriginal peoples, the cargo was not something manufactured or grown in another country. Rather it was a gift from the gods who, it seemed, specially favoured the Europeans. It became important to learn why this was so and European behaviour was closely observed and mimicked.

When the troops withdrew at the end of the war, the native peoples cleared areas of jungle to build 'landing strips' that they decorated with wooden model aeroplanes. They then conducted ritual enactments of European behaviour, convinced that such religious observance would persuade the gods to bring them cargo.

This is an example of a phenomenon which has become known as 'cargo cultism'. When the prophecies of their leaders about incoming cargo fail to materialize, cargo cults eventually weaken and disband. But it's easy to understand what happens before they do. Faced with technology so advanced that it's beyond their understanding, the native peoples decide that the 'miracles' they witness in the delivery of goods must be the work of supernatural beings – the gods.

Von Daniken simply suggested that today's major world religions are elaborate cargo cults developed in response to extra-terrestrial encounters now long forgotten.

It was a fascinating idea. The big question was, could he prove it?

Aliens and the Old Testament

▶Von Daniken's interest was drawn to what he saw as a significant peculiarity. The God of the Old Testament, later adopted by Christianity, was supposed to be the one and only God there was. It was this fact that made Judaism and Christianity unique in a world of pagan religions worshipping many gods. Yet in the Old Testament, God insisted on speaking of himself in the plural using phrases like 'Let us make man in our image'.

This peculiarity was compounded by two extremely strange passages in Genesis. The first, quoted at the beginning of this chapter, was:

And it came to pass when men began to multiply on the face of the earth and daughters were born unto them, that the sons of God saw the daughters of men that they were fair; and they took them wives of all which they chose.

Genesis VI: verses 1 and 2.

The second, from Genesis VI: verse 4 read:

There were giants on the Earth in those days; and also after that when the sons of God came in unto the daughters of men and they bore children to them, the same became mighty men which were of old, men of renown.

Von Daniken saw in both these quotations evidence of extra-terrestrial contact. Giant aliens, believed to be 'sons of God' by the ancient Hebrew chroniclers, visited Earth and actually interbred with primitive humanity to produce what was effectively a new, more advanced race.

It transpired in later books that von Daniken believed there were two visitations, thousands of years apart. A space-faring civilization accidentally discovered Earth at a time when life, but not intelligence, had evolved here. The aliens realized that there was the possibility of giving evolution a helping hand and conducted genetic experiments with a handful of apes. The aliens returned generations later and selected the best of these artificially-developed hominids to become *Homo sapiens*, our own race.

In one of these later books, *Gold of the Gods*, von Daniken developed the theme further to include the idea of a war going on between two different sets of extra-terrestrials, giving rise to Biblical descriptions (in the Book of Revelation) of a 'war in heaven' between the good angels, led by God, and evil angels led by Lucifer.

Once you know what you're looking for, von Daniken claims, there are many clues to the early existence of advanced technology in the Bible. One of the most spectacular is the destruction of Sodom and Gomorrah.

The story of the destruction is told in Genesis. Sodom and Gomorrah were twin cities situated on the great plain of Jordan. Lot and his family, kinspeople of Abraham and favourites of the Lord, went to live in Sodom despite the reputation both cities had for sinful behaviour.

Eventually the wickedness of these cities became so extreme that the Lord decided to destroy them. The Bible then describes a bargaining session during which Abraham persuaded the Lord that if he found as few as ten righteous men living in the cities He would spare them from destruction.

The Lord sent two angels into Sodom, apparently to search out ten righteous men. Lot recognized them for what they were and invited them to stay overnight in his home. The angels accepted, but the house was attacked by a mob and the occupants only escaped when the angels struck the ringleaders blind.

The incident confirmed the Lord's decision. The angels told Lot the cities would be destroyed and urged him and his family to leave with the words, 'Escape for thy life; look not behind thee, neither stay thou in all the plain; escape to the mountain, lest thou be consumed.'

For some reason Lot was afraid to go to the mountains and, with the agreement of the angels, took his family to the neighbouring city of Zoar. As he entered the city at dawn...

> *Then the LORD rained upon Sodom and upon Gomorrah brimstone and fire from the LORD out of heaven; And he overthrew those cities, and all the plain, and all the inhabitants of the cities, and that which grew upon the ground. But his (Lot's) wife looked back from behind him, and she became a pillar of salt. And Abraham went up early in the morning to the place where he stood before the LORD: And he looked toward Sodom and Gomorrah, and toward all the land of the plain, and beheld, and, lo, the smoke of the country went up as the smoke of a furnace. And it came to pass, when God destroyed the cities of the plain, that God remembered Abraham, and sent Lot out of the midst of the overthrow, when he overthrew the cities in the which Lot dwelt.*
>
> Genesis 19: v. 24–29

With Zoar now destroyed as well, Lot and his two daughters were forced to live in a cave in his dreaded mountains.

Von Daniken's readers learned this story was not what

it seemed. If you substitute extra-terrestrial for 'angel' and Leader for Lord, the whole thing takes on a new perspective. What actually destroyed the sinful cities was not the direct wrath of God, but a nuclear explosion. The angel was impatient for Lot and his wife to get out quickly because the countdown had already started. Those who were to be saved had to be taken quickly into the mountains which would offer protection against blast and radiation. But, as von Daniken put it, Lot's wife was destroyed when she 'turned and looked into the atomic sun'.

More evidence of extra-terrestrial landings was found by von Daniken in the Book of Ezekiel. He gave the relevant quote as follows:

Now it came to pass in the thirtieth year, in the fourth month, in the fifth day of the month, as I was among the captives by the river of Chebar, that the heavens were opened. And I looked and, behold, a whirlwind came out of the north, a great cloud, and a fire enfolding itself and a brightness was about it and out of the midst thereof as the colour of amber, out of the midst of the fire. Also out of the midst thereof came the likeness of four living creatures. And this was their appearance; they had the likeness of a man. And every one had four faces and every one had four wings. And their feet were straight feet; and the sole of their feet was like the sole of a calf's foot: and they sparkled like the colour of burnished brass.

Ezekiel I: v. 1–7

The Old Testament went on to describe the 'four living creatures' as follows:

Now as I beheld the living creatures, behold one wheel upon the earth by the living creatures, with his four faces. The appearance of the wheels and their work was like unto the colour of a beryl: and they four had one likeness: and their appearance and their work was as it were a wheel in the middle of a wheel. When they went, they went upon their four sides: and they turned not when they went. As for their wings, they were so high that they were dreadful; and their wings were full of eyes round about them four. And when the living creatures went, the wheels went by them: and when the living creatures were lifted up from the earth, the wheels were lifted up.

Ezekiel 1: v. 15–19

Both passages are certainly descriptions of something very odd, as is this further fragment quoted by von Daniken:

Then the spirit took me up, and I heard behind me a voice of a great rushing, saying, Blessed be the glory of the LORD from his place. I heard also the noise of the wings of the living creatures that touched one another, and the noise of the wheels over against them, and a noise of a great rushing.

Ezekiel 3: v. 12–13

Von Daniken suggested that the descriptions were clearly that of some sort of mechanical vehicle and the rushing noise the sound of its engines. Which led to the question, who spoke to Ezekiel? Not God, nor even gods. Supernatural beings have no need of mechanical transport, he argued.

Interesting though such speculation might be, it's

probably fair to say it would not, on its own, have propelled *Chariots of the Gods?* into the bestseller lists. But von Daniken didn't stop there. He began to present hard evidence.

Strange goings-on around the world

- On the Nasca plateau in Peru there is a network of lines and gigantic artworks depicting – among other things – birds, lizards, geometrical patterns and even a spider. The Nasca lines are drawn on such a scale you can only see what they represent from the air. What von Daniken saw was the remains of an ancient airfield, probably for interplanetary craft.

- On Easter Island, a tiny isolated speck in the Pacific, giant stone heads stare out to sea. The stone is so hard that simple tools could never have freed it from the bedrock of the quarries. Nor, since there are no trees on Easter Island, could rollers have been made to move the figures once they were quarried. Yet the figures are there to this day, clear testimony that advanced technology was used to raise them.

- The 2.3 million blocks of the Great Pyramid of Egypt were beyond the primitive quarrying technology of the ancients. Like Easter Island, Egypt had no wood, so there was no way of moving them. Nor could blocks weighing up to 70 tonnes be raised into position without modern lifting gear. To enhance the suggestion that advanced technology built the pyramids, von Daniken points out that the interior passages of the pyramid show no smoke marks. Electric light must have been used.

- The Nile island of Elephantine was named in ancient times for its similarity to an elephant but the shape of the island is only visible from the air. How did the ancients know it looked like an elephant?

- In Palenque, Mexico, there is an ornate carving on a sarcophagus lid of an astronaut flying a spaceship.
- A rustproof pillar in a Delhi temple is an example of an ancient metal alloy now unknown.
- Egyptian mummification practices were so advanced that they appear to have been designed to prepare the bodies for revival by the space gods on their return, rather as some people today freeze bodies for revival when science has advanced enough to do so.
- A massive system of gigantic tunnels under Ecuador and Peru, personally visited by von Daniken, contained among other things furniture made from a plastic-like material and a library of several thousand metal plaques which might contain the history of humanity and details of a lost prehistoric civilization.

These and other examples of his extensive research helped sell 25 million copies of von Daniken's books worldwide.

But scientists weren't quite so impressed by the evidence as the reading public.

The facts

➤Two scientists – the American astrophysicist Morris Jessup and the Russian ethnologist M. M. Agrest – both anticipated von Daniken in the 1950s by proposing there might be some connection between certain events described in the Bible and visitations by extra-terrestrials.

But these theories cut no ice at all with the scientific community as a whole. Jessup and Agrest were simply ignored. Von Daniken was accused of misinterpreting, exaggerating and, finally, faking his evidence.

- **Why did God speak of Himself in the plural?**
  According to historians, this is no more than the 'royal we' used by, among others, Her Majesty the Queen. The custom began in Ancient Persia and was fully accepted by the Hebrews who wrote Genesis. These scribes, in any case, would have been familiar with the religious idea that God took counsel from a heavenly host.

- **Who were the giants and the 'sons of God'?**
  Not one and the same people as von Daniken suggested. According to theologians, 'sons of God' was the term commonly used to describe members of the heavenly court. The giants were the *Nephilim*, human heroes of great size, believed in many ancient cultures to be the result of divine marriage. But 'divine marriage' is part of the world's rich mythology, not a veiled reference to a mating with extra-terrestrials. Biologists deny the possibility that extra-terrestrials could breed with humanity. A lion might, under rare circumstances, mate with a tigress to produce a liger, but genetic differences are too extreme to allow it to reproduce with a horse, an alligator or a duck-billed platypus. And these differences are tiny compared with the genetic differences of a wholly alien species. The chances of evolution producing two absolutely compatible species on different planets are 10 to the power of 16,557,000. This figure is so enormous it would add a further thousand pages to this book to write it out in full.

- **Could aliens have used genetic engineering on early hominids?**
  It's an interesting idea, but one that denies the evidence of the fossil record which shows a slow evolutionary development, not a sudden breakthrough.

- **Did an H-bomb destroy Sodom and Gomorrah?**
  Not possible, say archaeologists. These cities were built in the Great Rift Valley which runs all the way from Palestine into Africa. They certainly were destroyed suddenly, but the cause was a catastrophic earthquake that triggered explosions of natural gas around 2000 BC. The Biblical description of the event doesn't even sound like an atomic blast. Where, for example, is there mention of the mushroom cloud that's one of the most obvious characteristics of atomic explosions?

- **What about Lot's wife?**
  Von Daniken never made much sense about this in the first place, say his critics. According to the Bible, Lot's wife was supposed to have been turned into a pillar of salt, not vaporized by a nuclear explosion. Jebel Usdum, a range of hills near the Dead Sea, is composed mainly of rock salt and blocks of it take on strange shapes. Some of them even look like statues. One such block is called 'Lot's Wife' to this day.

- **Did Ezekiel see a spacecraft landing?**
  Ezekiel was an Old Testament prophet, prone to visions and mystic trances. Ezekiel himself says as much in the first verse of the first chapter of the Book that bears his name:

Now it came to pass in the thirtieth year, in the fourth month, in the fifth day of the month, as I was among the captives by the river of Chebar, that the heavens were opened, and I saw visions of God.

Interestingly, von Daniken omitted the last six words from his version of the quote.

The 'four living creatures', far from being extra-terrestrials, are similar to mythic composites found in religious art throughout the ancient world. Their only connection with outer space is that they may have had astrological associations with the Zodiac.

- **Is the Nasca Plain an airfield?**
Not unless the ancient astronauts were led by Dumb and Dumber. The soft, sandy soil would bog down any aircraft and several of the so-called 'landing strips' run straight into ridges and hills.

- **Were the giant heads of Easter Island raised by aliens?**
The anthropologist Thor Heyerdahl organized a party of seven locals who managed the 'impossible' job of quarrying a stone block with primitive stone tools in just three days. He estimated the carving of the finished statue would take about a year. Heyerdahl also showed conclusively that the statues could be erected without the aid of modern machinery.

Even von Daniken's claim about the lack of wood on Easter Island turned out to be less than the whole truth. Wood is certainly scarce today, but the island was forested when the statues were originally put up.

- ## How about the Great Pyramid?
  As a feat of engineering, the Great Pyramid is close to miraculous, but there's no mystery about how it was built. Archaeologists have successfully quarried blocks using the same tools used in Ancient Egypt. (The latest demonstration of the method was for a television programme.)

  The Greek historian Herodotus recorded that the massive blocks were raised by the use of levers and while Egyptologists found this difficult to believe, the English master builder Peter Hodges confirmed the method experimentally. Using levers, it needed just two men to lift a two and a half tonne mass. Hodges calculated that four men, each with a lever, would take only about ten pushes to raise a standard block up one step of the pyramid. Heavier stones would have required more levers and more pushes, but could have been moved in exactly the same way.

  To claim Egypt had no wood is simply untrue. Extensive imports added to home-grown supplies. The lack of smoke marks in the pyramid's interior passages was due not to electric light, but to the use of sesame-oil lamps, which burn without a smoky residue.

- ## How did the ancients know Elephantine Island looks like an elephant?
  They didn't and it doesn't. The island looks more like a mummified cat than an elephant. The name is not associated with the shape, but with the trade in ivory once conducted there.

- ## What about the Mexican spaceship?
  If it's a spaceship, it's got a quetzal bird nesting on the nose-cone. Archaeologists familiar with the Mayan

culture of Ancient Mexico see the carving as a composite of familiar symbols and glyphs specifying the burial of a Mayan noble in AD 683.

- **What's the alloy in the rustless Delhi pillar?**
  There isn't one. The pillar is made from iron. It doesn't rust because the metal was carefully refined to remove all impurities, a labour-intensive process, but one well within the known technology of the time.

- **Is there anything in the idea of space gods reviving Egyptian mummies?**
  Egyptian mummification techniques included the removal of the brain, internal organs and intestines before stuffing the body cavity full of aloes. It's difficult to imagine what sort of life a revived mummy would have without its bowels or brains and its backside stuffed with plants.

- **How about the plastic furniture in the Peruvian tunnels?**
  Von Daniken claimed he went with explorer Juan Moricz into the tunnels. Moricz told a reporter from the German magazine *Der Spiegel* this wasn't true. As far as Moricz was concerned, von Daniken had never been in the caves 'unless it was in a flying saucer'. A geology professor investigated the caves of the area, but found no artificial tunnels and no amazing artefacts. An official investigation by the Ecuadorean government was no more successful.

So it went on with the scientists demolishing virtually every claim von Daniken made. But von Daniken continued to write and millions of readers continued to believe there was something in what he said. Perhaps more importantly, other writers with higher standards of scholarship appeared to support the idea of ancient astronauts. The American Zecharia Sitchin, for example, examined a broad cross-section of ancient texts far less familiar to the general public than von Daniken's Biblical references and came to the conclusion that we were visited by space people in the distant past.

What has remained lacking is hard evidence. While some ancient texts *might* refer to astronauts, nobody has yet found a rusting spaceship buried in the ruins of Jericho or any other archaeological site.

The energy problem

▶Whatever the evidence, or lack of it, for ancient astronauts, most scientists remain sceptical about visitors from space *as a matter of principle*. The problem is the distances between the stars. These distances are measured in light-years, each representing some 5,865,696,000,000 miles.

The nearest star in our galaxy is Alpha Centauri, which is 4.3 light-years away. Astronomers have no reason to believe this system is inhabited. In 1996, they did discover a planet theoretically capable of supporting life. It orbits 70 Virginis, which is 50 light-years away.

In 1961, the Nobel prize-winning physicist Edward Purcell wrote a special report for the Atomic Energy Commission in which he worked out the energy needed to power spacecraft that could travel at a worthwhile fraction of the speed of light. The figure was so enormous he concluded no civilization, however advanced, could possibly afford it.

The idea, he said, belonged on the back of cereal packets.

This quote on UFOs is taken from _Funk and Wagnall's Encyclopedia_.

The objects most often mistaken for UFOs are bright planets and stars, aircraft, birds, balloons, kites, aerial flares, peculiar clouds, meteors, and satellites. The remaining sightings most likely can be attributed to other mistaken sightings or to inaccurate reporting, hoaxes, or delusions...

Funk and Wagnall's Encyclopedia, 1995 edition.

Do you think we should believe it?

= Section Six =
FLYING SAUCERS HAVE LANDED?

Kenneth Arnold was a respected US businessman and spare-time civilian pilot. He was one of a number of flyers helping search for a transport aircraft that had crashed somewhere in Washington State. His plane was crossing Mount Rainier, at 5,246 m the highest mountain in the Cascade Range, when he saw nine disc-shaped objects speed past in two parallel lines.

This happened in 1947, two years after the end of World War Two, when aircraft were a lot less sophisticated than they are today. Arnold was baffled by what he saw. He tried to get a closer look, but the discs were moving far too fast. He did a quick calculation of their speed and found to his astonishment they were moving in the region of 1,600 miles per hour. This was not only faster than his own little single-engined plane, it was faster – by far – than the most advanced aircraft anywhere in the world at that time.

Arnold reluctantly gave up the chase. When he landed, he reported his sighting to Air Traffic Control, who were as bewildered as he was. The story of the mysterious disc-shaped aircraft eventually leaked out to the press and when Arnold was interviewed about them, he described the way they flew as 'like a saucer would if you skipped it across the water'.

The press loved that description. Headlines started to appear about 'flying saucers'. The term stuck and is still in widespread use today.

Ancient saucers

➤Flying saucers aren't new and weren't even new in 1947. Unidentified flying objects, or UFOs, have been seen in the sky throughout history. In 234 BC, for example, three were reported in the sky over Rimini, in Italy, the first of many such sightings over the next century or so.

These reports, recorded by the Roman historian Pliny more than two thousand years ago, are not the first. In ancient China, bright discs in the sky were known as 'fiery dragons' and the paths they flew carefully charted on the ground. Nobody was allowed to build on a 'dragon path' and only the Emperor could be buried beneath one. There are even rock paintings in Africa that look suspiciously like flying saucers, suggesting the phenomenon actually started sometime in the depths of prehistory.

Whenever they were first seen, UFOs seem to have been a fact of human experience in every century and most countries. Frescoes on the walls of a fourteenth-century church in the former Yugoslavia show strange aircraft (interestingly with little men inside) at a time when the only things that flew were birds and bats. Medieval paintings show the panic caused in European populations by processions of luminous discs in the sky.

In the seventeenth century, UFOs were seen over Flüelen, Switzerland, in 1619 and over Worcester, England, in 1661. In the eighteenth century, they were back again over England (1704) and Switzerland (same year) but before the century was out, sightings had been reported in Italy, Scotland, Norway, Portugal and France.

With improved record-keeping, the reported sightings of UFOs in the nineteenth century turned into a flood. The first was in February 1802 when a German astronomer observed a dark disc crossing the sun. This was quickly followed by reports from Italy, Britain, Portugal and France. The last of these sightings, over Embrun in south-eastern France, was particularly interesting since formations of UFOs flew above the town in a dead straight line before turning suddenly at right-angles to fly off, again in a dead straight line.

In 1821, a luminous disc was spotted crossing the English Channel. More reports – several filed by professional astronomers – followed from Switzerland, Germany, the United States, Canada, Chile, Sicily, France and India.

One of the most spectacular sightings occurred on 18 June 1885 when three luminous discs arose out of the sea just half a mile from HMS *Victoria*, then steamed at 36°40'N latitude, 13°44'E longitude. These things were enormous – some observers claimed they were five times as big as the Moon – and were seen over a distance of 900 miles.

Still the reports of sightings continued: from Italy, from China, the USA, England, Scotland, Switzerland, France. The Great Exhibition in London's Hyde Park in 1851 was punctuated by a procession of flying discs that lasted from 9.30 in the morning until 3.30 on the afternoon of 4 September.

There were many more sightings worldwide before one of the most fantastic observations ever was reported simultaneously from Austria, Hungary and Silesia (now south-western Poland). Astronomers witnessed a 'glowing projectile' separate itself from the disc of the planet Mars and shoot towards Earth, where it exploded in the upper atmosphere.

In France, the prestigious periodical *L'Année Scientifique* ('The Scientific Year') reported that a 'vast number' of flying bodies crossed the disc of the Moon during 1874. Between then and 1882, there were UFO reports from Hungary, France, Wales, the Persian Gulf, Russia, Indiana and Connecticut, USA, England, Holland and Belgium.

In 1883, the inevitable happened. UFOs finally got photographed.

On 12 August of that year, a Mexican astronomer named José Bonilla was observing the sun from Zacatecas

Observatory when he saw a procession of some 143 UFOs on an oblique course across the face of the sun. When the procession appeared again next day he was ready for it and took photographs with a newly-invented camera attached to his telescope. His prints showed not only discs, but cigar- and spindle-shaped flying objects. In a report of his sightings, Dr Bonilla estimated that the objects had passed over the Earth at a height of 322,000 km.

These were the world's first photographs of UFOs, but certainly not the last. The sightings continued right throughout the remainder of the century from places as far apart as Chile, Vietnam, China, South Africa and Ireland. But now they were no longer confined to a few lonely astronomers. In April 1897, literally thousands of people throughout the United States reported seeing huge airships over farms and towns. A man named Walter McCann of Rogers Park, Illinois, took photographs of one of them. They show a hovering cigar-shaped craft.

This is not, of course, to say that the reports listed were sightings of spacecraft or even that they were all necessarily true. The best that can be said is that for a very long time people have been seeing strange things in our skies – and the reports started long before there were things like aeroplanes and weather balloons to confuse the picture.

Twentieth century

►There was no let-up in UFO sightings as the nineteenth century gave way to the twentieth. By April 1901, the UFOs were back, in the form of luminous wheels, over the Persian Gulf. This was followed a few years later by sightings in the Gulf of Oman and the Malacca Strait.

In 1909 came the first report of a landing. On 18 May, a Cardiff man named Lithbridge was walking in the Caerphilly

FLYING SAUCERS HAVE LANDED?

Mountains in Wales when he came upon a large cylindrical vehicle parked by the side of a lonely road. There were two 'peculiar looking men' inside it who became excited when they saw him. The craft flew off silently, leaving a depression in the grass where it had stood.

So it went on. Sightings' reports came from Boston, USA, Limerick, Ireland, and the South China Sea. A sighting over Elstree, England coincided with the start of World War I. The UFOs continued to appear throughout the war (including one that was watched for five hours over Ireland) and showed no sign of disappearing when peace was restored.

Nor did they disappear during World War II. Both sides in the conflict reported 'foo fighters' buzzing their planes. These disc-shaped craft were believed to be Nazi secret weapons by the Allies and Allied secret weapons by the Nazis.

While Kenneth Arnold is often credited with making the first flying saucer sighting, the reality is there have been mysterious things crossing our planet's skies since the dawn of time.

The question is, what are they?

Saucer landing

▶Arnold never suggested the saucers were alien spacecraft. In fact, he eventually went on record with the opinion that they weren't. He thought they might be natural phenomena. Others weren't so sure. Only five years after the Mount Rainier sighting came the first claim of an alien contact.

The man who made it was an American named George Adamski.

When Lithbridge saw his UFO landed beside the road

in Wales, he seems to have believed it was some sort of early flying machine, probably developed in a foreign country. Adamski's experience was very different.

In a book he later co-authored[4], he described how the spaceship came down ten miles from California's Desert Centre on the afternoon of 20 November 1952:

> *My attention was attracted by a flash in the sky and almost instantly a beautiful small craft appeared to be drifting through a saddle between two of the mountain peaks and settling silently into one of the coves about half a mile from me... Only the lower portion settled below the crest, while the upper, or dome section, remained above the crest and in full sight...*[5]

Adamski had a Kodak Box Brownie with him and took several photographs. They show a bell-shaped UFO with several spheres sticking out from its bottom surface. Adamski claimed it was about 13 m in diameter, made from 'translucent metal', with portholes and a lens, or possibly a light, on top of the dome-shaped cabin. The spheres underneath appeared to be part of the landing-gear.

An alien from Venus

►After taking his pictures, Adamski just stood there for a few minutes until his attention was drawn to a man motioning to him from the entrance of a ravine between two low hills about a half a kilometre away. Adamski walked over.

As he approached, he could see the man was smaller than he was and a lot younger — perhaps about 28 years old. He wore a chocolate-brown ski suit and his hair reached to his shoulders. He was extraordinarily handsome. The man took four steps forward until he was within arm's length of Adamski, at which point any small reservations Adamski had about him vanished.

> *Now for the first time I fully realized that I was in the presence of a man from space – A HUMAN BEING FROM ANOTHER WORLD! ... I was so stunned by this sudden realization that I was speechless.*[6]

Fortunately speechlessness didn't matter. After a greeting in which the palms of their hands were placed together, the alien began to converse with Adamski in a mixture of sign language and telepathy.

The man indicated that he came from the planet Venus and was concerned about atomic test explosions on Earth which were affecting the environment of space. In a curious pantomime during which the alien said 'Boom!' several times, he communicated to Adamski that if too many nuclear explosions took place, they would destroy all plant and animal life on Earth.

In answer to one of Adamski's questions, the alien told him space people were heading Earthwards from other planets in the solar system and from star systems elsewhere in the galaxy. These space people never landed in populated parts of our planet, partly because they didn't want to start a panic, partly because they were worried about being torn to pieces.

Adamski asked how many planets of our solar system were inhabited. The alien indicated that they all were.

After some further 'conversation' (during which the alien acknowledged belief in God) they strolled together to the spaceship and the Venusian took off.

Unreliable info

➤As we've already seen, the information Adamski got from the alien was rubbish.

The creature, with his zipperless ski suit and his size 9 shoes, was to all outward appearances human – a spaceman rather than the sort of alien that used to chase Sigourney Weaver in the film *Alien*. Yet he claimed to come from Venus, a planet with a surface temperature hot enough to melt lead, and insisted every planet in the solar system was inhabited, when space probes clearly show they are nothing of the sort.

Even in the early 1950s when our knowledge of the solar system was a lot less than it is today, there were questions asked about how an alien managed to survive in Earth's atmosphere without a pressure suit or helmet. Desmond Leslie, who co-authored Adamski's book, was forced to conclude things were not exactly as they seemed. He told me some years later he thought Adamski's visitor had actually come from the 'astral plane' of Venus.

Adamski's critics were far less sympathetic. Many decided he was mad or simply lying. These conclusions were reinforced by the publication of a second book in which he claimed he'd been taken on a trip in a flying saucer which circled the Moon before dropping him back home again.

Problems with the evidence

➤All the same, there are problems with the theory that Adamski was just plain nuts. Almost all his critics ignore the fact he was not alone when he met his 'Venusian'. There were six people with him, all of whom signed affidavits swearing they had also seen the craft and its pilot. Only one of the six, George Hunt Williamson, followed Adamski's example in writing a book (in fact several books) on UFOs and related subjects. The rest seem to have got little from swearing their affidavits except public ridicule.

There were other things ignored as well.

Earth is surrounded by rings of high energy particles. These rings are now called the Van Allen radiation belts, after James A. Van Allen of the University of Iowa, who headed the team of scientists that discovered them.

First evidence of the belts came from a Geiger counter reading in the US satellite, Explorer 1, launched on 31 January 1958. Adamski was talking about radiation belts around the Earth in 1953. How did he know?

If the belts were the only thing he knew about, we might be happy to dismiss it as coincidence. But Adamski mentioned other things as well. For example he talked about 'fireflies' in space visible from the window of the flying saucer that took him on his trip around the Moon. Real fireflies can't live in space, of course, but John H. Glenn, the first US astronaut to circle the Earth in 1962, confirmed an unexpected electrical phenomenon surrounding his craft that gave the appearance of fireflies.

Adamski also knew about a curious glow of light beyond the stratosphere confirmed by astronauts L. Gordon Cooper, Jr., on the last flight of the Mercury programme in 1963, and Walter Marty Schirra, Jr., command pilot of the Gemini 6 mission which made the first rendezvous in space in 1965.

Again the question arises: how did Adamski know?

The investigation

➤It's probably safe to say Adamski's experience was

considered too outrageous for any serious scientific investigation. But Kenneth Arnold's original report was not. Just a year after the massive publicity about the Mount Rainier sightings, the United States created Project Sign to investigate the reports that were now beginning to flood in.

Project Sign was renamed Project Grudge then Project Blue Book.

At first, Project Blue Book confined itself merely to collecting and recording UFO reports. But then in 1952, just four months before Adamski met his alien, witnesses reported UFO activity near the National Airport in Washington, DC. This sort of report was commonplace enough by now and probably would not have led to action but for the fact that, for the first time ever, the saucer sightings were simultaneously confirmed on radar. There was something solid up there and it was too near the National Airport for comfort.

The US government quietly set up a panel of scientists headed by physicist Professor H.P. Robertson, from the California Institute of Technology. The panel included engineers, meteorologists, physicists and one astronomer. It was organized by the CIA, briefed on US military activities and told to work in secret. The American Government had clearly decided UFOs represented a potential threat to national security.

But did they?

The result

➤The concentration of sightings in the United States soon spread outwards and reports began to come in from Britain, Europe, the USSR (as it was called then), Australia and even, less frequently, Asia. Early in 1966, a second scientific panel was created to continue and expand the work of the first. It was led by Dr Edward Condon, a former head of the American Association for the Advancement of Science and probably the country's most prestigious physicist. This panel also met in secret.

When the report of Project Blue Book was eventually declassified, it was a bit of a disappointment. In the nearly nineteen years between 1947 and 1969, a massive 12,618 UFO reports were received. All but 5.6% of them were explained by such factors as bright planets, meteors, auroras, ion clouds, aircraft, birds, balloons, searchlights, hot gases, or unusual meteorological conditions.

But while it sounded small, the unexplained 5.6% accounted for a massive 701 sightings.

The report concluded that 'no UFO reported, investigated, and evaluated by the Air Force has ever given any indication of threat to our national security'.

> ## The threat

►This Blue Book Project conclusion was rather at odds with what happened on 5 October 1960, when a missile formation was picked up by American early-warning radar at Thule in north-west Greenland.

As their course was charted, worried personnel discovered the blips on their screens had originated somewhere over the Soviet Union and were heading directly for the United States. There was an immediate red telephone alert to Strategic Air Command Headquarters in Omaha, Nebraska.

US forces worldwide went on to an immediate Code Red nuclear alert. Fighter planes were scrambled in every military airfield. B-52 bombers, already in the air as part of the country's standing nuclear deterrent, were given their preliminary codes. It only required one more signal to send them deep into the heart of the Soviet Union and start the Third World War that, most scientists agreed, would destroy life on this planet.

Strategic Air Command demanded urgent confirmation of the incoming missiles. Tension peaked abruptly when it was realized all lines of communication with Thule were dead. Word spread that this outpost of the early-warning system had already been destroyed.

By now US ground radar had picked up the missile formation. An urgent phone call went through to the President. The world teetered on the brink of nuclear war.

Then the 'missiles' changed course and disappeared.

After minutes of sheer disbelief, the global nuclear alert stood down. Subsequent investigation showed commun-ications with Thule had been cut not by a missile strike but by an iceberg. The 'missiles' were in fact UFOs.

The Condon report

►The second panel of experts, led by Dr Condon, investigated 59 cases in the two years following its formation. More than a third of them were unexplained.

But Condon issued a final report in 1969 which concluded UFO study had added nothing to scientific knowledge and absolutely dismissed the possibility that the saucers were evidence of extra-terrestrial life. The Air Force apparently agreed and ceased all official investi-gation of UFOs from that date. The key word here is 'official'. There are persistent claims that many govern-ments continue to investigate UFOs in secret and that their public statements of denial are part of a worldwide cover-up to avoid panic about what is actually a very mysterious and frightening situation.

Official dismissal has certainly done nothing to stem the

flood of reports. Since 1947 UFOs in their hundreds have appeared in nearly every country of the globe. The number of sightings is far higher than most people imagine. In 1973 a Gallup poll indicated that 11 per cent of the adult population in the United States had seen what they thought was a UFO. So far, more than 50,000 worldwide sighting reports have been computerized – a figure generally accepted to represent the very small tip of a very large iceberg.

Although many scientists still cling to the opinion that anyone who sees a UFO is probably hallucinating, study of these reports suggests that UFO sightings are random, and no pattern of UFO witnesses has been found. Witnesses cut across economic, class, racial, and educational lines and include at least one American President.

Is there something real up there, something that has been watching humanity for centuries?

Something that is watching still…?

Meet Barney and Betty Hill.

They were abducted by extra-terrestrials.

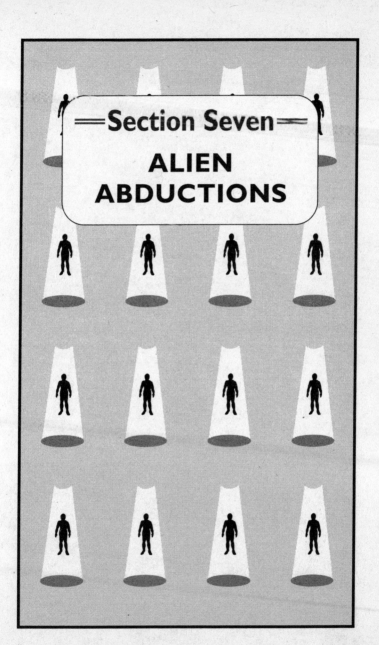

=Section Seven=
ALIEN ABDUCTIONS

George Adamski's published account of meeting with an alien was followed by others no less remarkable.

In 1954, Truman Bethurum published *Aboard a Flying Saucer,* which told of his meeting with smallish, olive-skinned aliens from Clarion, a planet they claimed was perpetually hidden behind the Moon. The captain of their spaceship, a massive 109-m vehicle, was Aura Rhanes – a woman whom Bethurum described as 'tops in shapeliness and beauty'. She and Bethurum became fast friends and spent a whole night swapping planet stories.

One of the most interesting things about Bethurum's book was his claim that the aliens sometimes moved unrecognized among humanity – he once saw the lovely Ms Rhanes drinking orange juice in a restaurant.

Daniel Fry followed more directly in Adamski's footsteps by meeting his alien A-lan (a.k.a. Alan) in a desert, this one in New Mexico rather than California. A-lan, who spoke American English, asked him to write a book warning the Earth about the risk of nuclear war.

The three pioneers were joined in 1955 by Orfeo Angelucci, who was taken on a saucer flight to Neptune, warned like Fry about the risky state of our planet and met Jesus, who turned out to be an extra-terrestrial.

It's difficult to imagine anyone could beat that, but Howard Menger managed it. Howard first made contact with an extra-terrestrial when he was only ten. His description of the alien leaves little to the imagination:

> *The curves of her lovely body were delicately contoured, revealing through the translucent material. Even though very young, the feeling I received was unmistakable...*[7]

Quite so. But this beauty turned out to be more than

500 years old.

Menger was eventually taken on a flight to Saturn where he learned Saturnian piano music and discovered he had himself been a Saturnian in an earlier life. In that lifetime while on a visit to Venus, he fell in love with a stunning Venusian girl named Marla. Coincidentally, this same Marla was now on an Earth mission in New Jersey.

Menger searched her out and married her in 1958.

It's fairly clear that much of the material in these 1950s reports is claptrap. Space probes have now shown there is no planet Clarion 'hidden behind the Moon' and even in the Fifties it was hard to believe in aliens who visited the neighbourhood restaurant to drink orange juice. Most psychologists would tell you that if a man claims he's met a beautiful blonde (female) alien, the chances are he's indulging in wishful thinking rather than telling the truth.

Contacts galore

▶But like reports of UFOs themselves, reports of alien contacts turned from a trickle into a flood.

Two sisters, Helen and Betty Mitchell, met with a couple of 'Space brothers from Mars' in a St Louis coffee shop.

Sixty-year-old Buck Nelson was cured of his arthritis by a flying-saucer ray that was brighter and hotter than the sun.

Brazilian Aladino Felix (who wrote under the pen-name Dino Kraspedon) had conversations with aliens from Io and met one disguised as a Protestant vicar.

Elizabeth Klarer was given an assignment by the British Government to investigate a 'highly advanced civilization from outer space' during World War II and subsequently gave birth to a son fathered by an extra-terrestrial.

Marian Keech was warned by aliens that a great flood was about to destroy Salt Lake City in Utah. The flood never materialized. Nor did the spaceship that was supposed to rescue Marian and a group of her followers.

But just when cynical observers were beginning to wonder how silly UFO contact reports could get, the news broke of what happened to Betty and Barney Hill.

The Hill case

➤Americans Betty and Barney Hill were on holiday in Canada in September 1961 when they heard reports of a hurricane that had struck the east coast of America and was predicted to move inland across the state of New Hampshire where they lived. They hadn't the money to stay longer in Canada and were worried that the storm might cut them off. They decided to make an immediate run for home, even though it would mean driving through the night.

Around 9 p.m. on the evening of 19 September, they crossed the US-Canadian border and took the US Route 3 highway south. They reached the town of Colebrook and stopped at a restaurant there. Shortly after ten, they were on their way again. Barney estimated it would take them four or five hours to get home. He expected to arrive between 2.30 and 3 a.m. next morning.

Shortly after they drove past the village of Lancaster, Betty noticed two bright lights near the Moon. One seemed to be getting larger. She pointed them out to Barney, who thought they might be a satellite that had gone off course.

The larger light stayed with them for several miles, appearing and disappearing behind mountains and treetops. Eventually Betty suggested they stop the car to let their dog Delsey have a run. She told Barney that if he pulled in somewhere that had a clear field of vision, they might be able to see what the light was.

Barney found a place, parked the car and he and Betty walked down the road with Delsey. The light was still there and seemed definitely to be moving. Betty went back to the car for their binoculars and managed to make out some sort of shape with flashing lights. Barney decided they were watching an aeroplane, or possibly a helicopter.

They went back to their car and drove off slowly. By now they were beginning to feel a little worried. The thing, whatever it was, seemed to be circling round them and there were no other cars on the road.

Betty took out the binoculars again. By now the UFO was close enough for her to see that it was some sort of enormous aircraft with a double row of windows. Barney stopped the car again, in the middle of the road this time, took the binoculars from Betty and got out. At first he still argued they were watching a plane, but then grew frightened. What he was seeing through the binoculars didn't look like a plane.

Barney started to walk towards the object, which dropped down to hover about treetop height. When he was about fifty metres away and still using the binoculars, he was able to see about a dozen people staring down at him from the mystery craft.

The UFO dropped in altitude and seemed to lower down some sort of ladder or ramp. Then one of the occupants emerged. Barney continued to watch the creatures in the craft. To his horror he found he was having difficulty looking away from their eyes, which seemed to exert a curious, almost hypnotic, influence over him.

Gripped by sudden panic, Barney screamed and ran back to the car. He drove off shouting that he was sure they were 'going to be captured'. But in fact nothing happened. Or almost nothing.

Neither Barney nor Betty could see the strange craft now, not even as a distant light. They heard a beeping sound and felt momentarily sleepy. Then came some further beeping sounds. The road seemed unfamiliar but when they saw a sign to Concord they realized where they were and drove directly home.

Oddly enough, they arrived home in daylight. Both their watches had stopped, but clocks in the house showed it was now 5 a.m., two to two and a half hours later than Barney had originally anticipated. During the journey, Betty had asked Barney, 'Now do you believe in UFOs?' But despite his fright, Barney told her he did not.

The Hills went to bed and slept exhausted until three that afternoon. When they woke, their experience the night before seemed unreal. But Betty examined their car and found several shiny circles, each about the size of a large coin, burned into the paintwork of the boot. A compass brought close to them spun wildly. It looked as if something very real had happened to them.

Much against Barney's better judgement, Betty reported their sighting to the local Air Force Base where details were logged. Betty also wrote to Major Donald Keyhoe, who had recently published a book about flying saucers.

Within days she had started to have nightmares of being seized and carried off in a UFO.

The investigation

►A month after the Hills had their frightening experience, the National Investigations Committee on Aerial Phenomena (NICAP) became involved. This Washington-based organization, directed by Major Keyhoe, avoided crank reports like the plague, but occasionally investigated the more serious and puzzling UFO sightings.

NICAP experts interviewed the Hills and were impressed. As word spread, other experts became involved. Betty was still having nightmares. Barney remained uncomfortable discussing his experience. Two suggestions were made to them. The first was that they should retrace the steps of their interrupted journey. The second was that hypnosis might help them recall more clearly what had happened.

The Hills took up the first suggestion and while their return trip to Route 3 triggered no further memories, they did discover something very interesting. When they called at a small restaurant near the town of Woodstock, local residents told them of several UFO sightings in the area. The descriptions of these UFOs – one of which hovered for almost an hour – sounded suspiciously like the craft they had seen.

It was not until February of 1964 that the Hills took up the second suggestion.

Hypnotic regression

►Hypnotic regression is the term used by psychiatrists to describe a technique by which hypnotized subjects are mentally taken back in time in order to remember things they have forgotten.

It's a peculiar feeling for the subject because it's usually less like remembering than reliving. When a subject is regressed to childhood, for example, her handwriting will change. So will her voice and the way she reacts to things. It's as if she actually *becomes* a child again. In this state she will vividly relive childhood experiences, right down to tiny details like the pattern on her mother's apron.

It was this technique that Dr Benjamin Simon, a well-known Boston psychiatrist, used on the Hills on 22 February 1964.

The story

▶Dr Simon regressed both Betty and Barney Hill in a series of sessions over a period of six months. The stories they told matched, but what they remembered under hypnosis was almost unbelievable. The reconstruction of the events of 19 September was roughly as follows:

Sometime after they saw the UFO, a group of between 8 and 11 small, grey men (or at least humanoids) with strange eyes, in matching uniforms and military-style caps stepped into the road and stopped their car. The leader – whom Barney thought was evil and likened to a Nazi – told them they would not be harmed.

Despite this reassurance, they were both taken on board a disc-shaped aircraft where they were physically examined. Samples of hair, fingernails and skin were taken and a long needle inserted into Betty's abdomen. They were eventually permitted to return to their car and continue the journey home.

During the two hours they were aboard the strange craft Betty asked the leader where he came from. He showed her a map of a distant star system.

The diagnosis

▶Many people found the Hill's story hard to believe. On the face of it, this seemed to be yet another 'encounter' with Flash Gordon-style aliens who claimed to come from the depths of the galaxy yet looked human, wore no spacesuits and had little difficulty breathing the terrestrial air.

But unlike Adamski, Menger, Bethurum and the others,

Barney and Betty Hill wrote no books, sought no publicity, established no cult following and made no wild claims about trips around the Moon. They were, if anything, embarrassed by their experience. Barney had particular problems with the story he told under hypnosis since, unlike Betty, he did not actually believe in flying saucers. Furthermore, their sternest critics were usually prepared to admit the Hills *believed* they were telling the truth. Their transparent honesty and common sense impressed everybody.

All the same, Dr Simon finally concluded their accounts were fantasy. He was not impressed by the fact that they tallied. He believed that Barney had heard details of Betty's nightmares (which were very similar to the hypnotic memories) and his unconscious mind had simply thrown them up again. From his wide experience as a psychiatrist, Dr Simon made one important point: hypnosis doesn't guarantee that people tell the truth, only that they tell what they *believe* to be the truth.

And there the case might have rested, but for one worrying detail.

The star map

►After one of her sessions with Dr Simon, Betty drew the star map she claimed the leader had shown her. There was nothing in the night sky that looked remotely like it and, like the rest of her story, it was dismissed as fiction.

But years after the event, in 1974, Dr Walter Mitchell, an astronomer at Ohio State University, collaborated with Marjory Fish, a health-physics technician at Oak Ridge National Laboratory, to take a fresh look at the evidence.

Ms Fish argued that if the map were genuine, it would be drawn from the viewpoint of the aliens' own solar system. Using a computer program created by Dr David Saunders, a member of the Condon Committee, Ms Fish and Dr Mitchell discovered that the map showed the night sky as seen not from Earth, but from the distant star Zeta Reticuli.

More puzzling details were to follow. Betty Hill accurately drew Zeta Reticuli as a *double* star, but this fact was not known, even to professional astronomers, in 1964. It was only discovered, by an astronomer named Van de Camp, nine years later. What's more, both Zeta Reticuli 1 and Zeta Reticuli 2 are now believed to support planetary systems that make them prime candidates for the evolution of extra-terrestrial life.

More abductions

▶Betty and Barney Hill were the first people in modern times to claim they had been abducted by aliens from another planet. But they were a long way from being the last.

In 1991, the Roper organization conducted a three-month survey that interviewed nearly six thousand Americans looking for abduction evidence. From case after case, a typical picture emerged. Here's what will happen if you're ever abducted:

The experience is most likely to start while you're at home or in a car. It'll be night or the early hours of the morning and your first hint that something's going on will be the appearance of a bright light.

Although you're wide awake, you won't feel fully in control. Your mind will get fuzzy, so when you tell people about it afterwards, they'll insist you were dreaming. But you'll know you aren't dreaming. You'll know something – some Thing – has taken control of you.

You'll probably be alone when it happens, although not

necessarily. In one case, two teenage girls disappeared together during the night from a basement den in one of their homes. Their parents were mounting a frantic search when they reappeared at 6 a.m. In another, an eight-year-old child confirmed her mother was missing at the time she (the mother) claimed to have been abducted. In a third, the room-mate of a college girl watched aliens abduct and return her friend ... before she herself was abducted.

You'll feel as if you're floating. You'll be approached by one or more small, grey humanoids with large heads and very large, almost nocturnal, eyes. You'll be carried – sometimes through solid walls – to a saucer- or dome-shaped craft and carried on board by a beam of light. Around this point, you'll find yourself paralysed except for your head and eyes, so you can still look around and see what's going on.

The craft you're in will rise from the ground to carry you to a second, much larger ship. Inside this ship you will find yourself in a brightly lit, sparsely furnished room with various unfamiliar instruments and what might be computer consoles. You can see several different types of aliens working at various tasks. These may include luminous creatures, entities that appear reptilian and even some beings that are semi-transparent, like ghosts.

You will be undressed – if you're lucky, you might be allowed to keep your T-shirt on – and made to lie down on a table where you will be studied like a medical specimen. Like Barney and Betty, tissue samples will be taken and weird metallic instruments used to probe every part of your body.

You may have to undergo several surgical operations, usually inside your skull. They'll use vibrationary techniques to keep you calm and dull the pain, although sometimes it can break through. When they're finished, they'll take you back to where they found you. You may or may not remember what just happened.

How many abductions?

▶When the Roper organization ran the results of their poll through their computer to find out what was happening in the country as a whole, the results were staggering.

Analysis showed that somewhere between several hundred thousand and several million Americans believe themselves to have been abducted by aliens.

Did this mean several million Americans are just plain mad?

Psychiatrists' opinions

▶Carl Gustav Jung, a psychiatrist who founded one of the most influential schools of psychology, believed UFOs were a projection of the human mind – essentially some weird sort of hallucination.

Abduction reports hadn't started to come in during Jung's lifetime, but many – probably most – practising psychiatrists today would explain them in much the same way. The general idea seems to be that while the experiences seem real enough to the people who have them, they are actually an unusual type of waking dream.

But there is one rather interesting dissenting voice.

Dr John E. Mack is Professor of Psychiatry at Harvard Medical School. In other words, he's the psychiatrist who teaches America's top psychiatrists. In 1989, he became interested in the abduction phenomenon and decided to investigate it for himself.

To the horror of his more conservative colleagues, he

concluded that many, if not most, of those who claim to have been carried off by aliens are not mad and not even deluded.

Professor Mack's professional opinion is that something really happened.

Where do the aliens come from?

►Betty Hill's star map suggests the saucers may be flown by pilots from the deep reaches of our galaxy. But where does that leave Dr Edward Purcell, the Nobel prize-winning physicist who claimed the energy needs of inter-stellar travel were far too high for even the most advanced civilization?

Dr Purcell made his cereal packet announcement in 1961. Since then, quantum physicists probing deep into the heart of matter have made a startling discovery. Even a total vacuum is not completely empty. At its most fundamental level it consists of seething quantum foam as subatomic particles wink briefly into existence before winking out again.

Scientists have now calculated that there is enough energy in a volume of 'empty' space the size of a light bulb to destroy our entire galaxy. If you used it really efficiently, you might even managed to destroy the universe. It looks as if there may be lots of energy for inter-stellar travel after all.

But despite star maps and quantum physics, Professor Mack is not at all convinced the aliens originate in outer space. He thinks they might come from a parallel universe.

This is a quote from the *Encyclopaedia Britannica*.

Fairy: also spelled FAERIE, or FAERY, in folklore, supernatural being, usually of diminutive human form, who magically intermeddles in human affairs.

Encyclopaedia Britannica, 1995

Doesn't it sound just a little like the aliens who keep abducting human beings?

Section Eight

PARALLEL UNIVERSE

Although not in the majority, a hefty percentage of physicists today believe there are alternative realities – whole universes, some like our own, some very different, that exist beyond the boundaries of the world that we experience.

The idea of different dimensions of reality has long been a favourite theme of science fiction, but modern scientists have taken to it not for its appeal to the imagination, but because they think it explains the peculiar results of a classical experiment.

The experiment was this:

On your right, a particle generator. You can imagine this as a gun that shoots a stream of tiny cannon-balls.

On your left, a target. This has a special surface that means you can record the impact of any little cannon-ball that hits it.

Between the two, a screen. There are two slits in the screen that you can open and close one at a time. When you close both slits, no cannon-balls can get through. When you open one slit, a certain number of cannon-balls get through. When you open both slits, twice as many cannon-balls get through.

Except that they don't.

When physicists actually carried out this experiment back in the 1930s, they found after they opened both slits, *fewer* particles hit the target than when they only opened one.

This made no sense at all so they tried the experiment again. The same result occurred.

> ## Many photons make light work

▶Light is made up of particles called photons. This means that an electric torch is a particle generator. Shine a torch into a dark corner and you're actually using one of those guns that shoots a stream of tiny cannon-balls. It's like something out of *Star Trek*.

Now that you have your particle generator, you can do a bit of the experiment for yourself.

Shine the torch through a pinhole in a card and you'll get a circle of light on any screen you set up on the far side.

Make two pinholes and you'll get two circles. Where they overlap you'll get dark and light stripes on the screen – what you're looking at is an interference pattern.

That's about as far as you can go with a torch and a card. But pretend you had some way to turn down the intensity of your torch so that it released only a single photon. You'd expect this photon to go through one pinhole or the other if both were open. You'd expect there would be only one (tiny) circle of light on the screen where the photon hit.

But what actually happens is that you still get the interference pattern. This isn't possible with just one photon, but it happens when both pinholes are open.

What's even more peculiar, you *don't* get the pattern when just one pinhole is open.

You can see right away this raises a couple of very tricky questions. The first is how a single photon manages to interfere with itself. The second is how it knows when two pinholes are open and not just one.

The great physicist, Albert Einstein, was suspicious of the double-slit experiment. When he was asked how the photon knew two pinholes were open, he said sourly that it must be telepathic.

Surfing the wave

➤Nobody actually knows what subatomic particles look

like. They're too small to show up under any microscope. Scientists have to try to work out their appearance by watching the way they behave.

When they saw how particles behaved in the double-slit experiment, they started to wonder if they were really dealing with little cannon-balls at all. Somebody came up with the idea that subatomic particles might actually be waves, exactly like the waves you see breaking on a beach.

So set up your experiment again, but this time don't imagine a gun shooting cannon-balls. Imagine a machine that makes waves and sends them towards the target.

You can see that solves the mystery. When you're dealing with a wave, it doesn't matter how many slits are open. Open one and the wave goes through one. Open two and the same wave goes through both. So you certainly wouldn't expect any more waves to hit the target.

In fact, since opening two slits splits the wave for a moment while it's passing through the screen, you could be pretty sure that a few of those split waves would accidentally collide and cancel each other out. That would mean with two slits open you'd get fewer hits on the target than with one. Which was exactly what had happened.

There was only one small problem. The particles behaved like waves while they were passing through the slit(s) in the screen. But they turned back into little cannon-balls when they struck the target.

Living with the impossible

►This seemed like another impossibility, but the incredulous physicists watched it happen. A wave striking the target would strike it all at once, like a wave breaking on a beach. But the particles always struck in particular places — just like little cannon-balls.

The scientists started to refer to *wave-particle duality* as if this explained something, and lived for years with the knowledge that particles behaved like cannon-balls in certain circumstances and like waves in others.

But questions remained in their minds.

Imaginary waves

▶After a while, scientists started to wonder if the 'wave' was really a wave or just something happening inside their heads so they could keep track of what they were seeing – an imaginary wave.

This is not as daft as it sounds.

Look through the window. If you live in the country, your eyes see trees, grass, fields, a stream and so on. If you live in a town, your eyes see houses, streets, traffic. But what's really happening isn't quite so simple. What's happening is that reflected light hits your eye, alerts receptors in your retina to trigger an electrical pulse along a nerve track which feeds information into your brain. It's your brain that's doing the seeing, not your eye.

Your brain is being peppered by information every second of the day. It works hard to organize that information so it makes sense to you. It does this by imposing *patterns* on the information – here's the pattern of a house, here's the pattern of grass and so on. It's this organizing function that allows you to recognize a flower, even if you've never seen that particular flower before.

So physicists started to think the whole wave-particle question was just a particular pattern their brains imposed on what they were watching. The 'wave' was really a collection of possibilities that behaved in a wave-like way.

In other words, the particle was still a little cannon-ball, but instead of simply watching the way this little cannon-ball behaved, you took account of all the various things that *could* happen to a little cannon-ball. Your mind organized these probabilities into something that looks, to you, like a wave.

Having dreamed this one up, the scientists started to walk about particles as *probability* waves.

Problem solved

►This looked as if it solved the problem.

Firstly, you're back with little cannon-balls. As each one gets close to the two open slits in the screen, the probability wave – which really only exists in your mind – shows the different possibilities open to the cannon-balls. It shows whether it passes through the top slit or the bottom slit, or strikes the screen and is absorbed or deflected. The wave doesn't tell you exactly where the cannon-ball will go, only where it's *most likely* to go.

Unless you're a nuclear physicist, chances are you've stopped following this by now. But that doesn't matter. What matters is the theory of probability waves neatly explained particle behaviour.

Except for one small thing. If these waves only existed inside your head, how did they manage to interfere with one another?

The answer to that turned out to be the explanation of the particle problem.

Parallel universes

►In 1957, a young American physicist named Hugh Everett III figured it all out. In an argument so simple you'd be amazed nobody thought of it before, he said that if two probabilities can interfere with one another, each of them must actually exist.

But since there's no way both probabilities can exist in our universe, it follows logically that there must be a second, parallel universe that contains the second probability.

Could a mouse change the universe?

►Was Dr Everett serious or had he been reading too much science fiction? Some of his colleagues thought – and still think – he must be right. Others clung – and still cling – to an alternative explanation.

The alternative explanation is even more far-fetched than a second universe. What happened in the double-slit experiment was that as soon as an observer looked at the probability wave, it collapsed. At that point, all those possibilities suddenly disappeared, leaving only one reality.

Einstein hated that explanation even more than he hated telepathic photons. He said he couldn't believe the universe would change just because a mouse looked at it.

But maybe that was because some of his own work pointed to a second universe as well.

Black holes

►No star burns for ever.

Our sun is destined one day to expand into a red giant, then contract into a small, cool shell known as a white dwarf.

If it were about three times bigger, something else would happen. Its own gravity would force it to collapse in on itself, getting smaller and smaller, more and more compact, until it became a neutron star, the most dense body in the universe.

If it were bigger still, something else would happen.

Something deadly.

It was a scientist named Schwarzchild who used Einstein's General Theory of Relativity to calculate that if a star is big enough, the collapse keeps going. The neutron star itself gets smaller and smaller. Gravity gets stronger and stronger. Eventually it gets so strong it holds in everything. Nothing can escape and that includes light.

The neutron star has turned into a black hole.

Black holes are creepy. Their gravity is so strong it warps space and time. Scientists calculate that a point inside exists, known as a singularity, where certain values reach infinity.

This seems impossible, but conditions are so extreme in there that scientists think it might actually be real, as opposed to a mistake in their calculations. If it is real, all bets are off. The laws of physics break down. Nobody has the least idea what *could be* happening, let alone what *is* happening.

Watch your step

►If you have the misfortune to fall into a black hole, by the time you reach the singularity, your volume will be reduced to zero (an impossibility, but never mind) and you'll have reached a place where space and time have literally ceased.

The calculations surrounding the singularity of a black hole run so far against the familiar laws of physics that scientists have begun to speculate on the possibility that you wouldn't really be reduced to zero volume at all, but rather 'sucked through' the fabric of space-time into a wholly different universe.

They won't speculate on what state you'd be in when you got there.

Many scientists don't like the idea of an alternative universe. Einstein himself saw his famous Theory of Relativity might point towards one but tended towards the belief that there was a flaw in his calculations. All the same, he had the courage to publish his findings in 1935. The paper was co-authored by his colleague Nathan Rosen. It highlighted something unexpected.

The calculations of Einstein and Rosen showed every black hole had to be paired with a white hole, an area of space in which matter and light were spewed out at the same rate as matter and light entered the black hole.

The problem was, the corresponding white hole could not exist in this universe. It was back to back with the black hole and had to be elsewhere – in another, separate reality. The crossover point between the black hole on this side and the white hole on the other side became known as an Einstein-Rosen bridge.

Putting another spin on it

➤Worse was to come. The idea that there are two (and only two) parallel universes arises out of calculations based on a static black hole. In the real world, black holes aren't static. Black holes are made from stars; and stars (most of them) spin on their axes. This means a black hole must be spinning too.

When you make the calculations for a spinning black hole (as the Australian physicist Roy P. Kerr did in 1963) you get a different result. A spinning black hole is the gateway not to one other parallel universe, but to an infinite number of parallel universes – and in theory you can get to all but one of them from this universe.

Wormholes

►There are very few physicists who'd lay odds on your chances of jumping through a black hole into another universe and getting there in one piece.

But another implication of relativity theory looks more promising.

Although Einstein's theories of relativity (he published two of them) were actually about gravity, the implications of their mathematics was much more far-reaching. They showed, for example, that there is no such thing as separate space and time. However we experience it, the universe is really a single unit combining the two. Einstein called it space-time. They also showed that space is curved, that nothing can be accelerated beyond the speed of light and that the faster you travel, the slower time passes.

These peculiar properties of space have given rise to the idea of a 'wormhole'. Physicist John Wheeler, who was the first to come up with the idea, describes a wormhole as a type of 'tube' that directly connects distant parts of the universe. If you imagine space curved to form a globe, you can get some idea of how a wormhole works. To get from the north pole to the south pole of the globe, you can go the long way round on the surface (which is the only way we know how to travel) but a wormhole might let you go through the middle – an altogether shorter journey.

And since you aren't just talking about space, but about space-time, the wormhole could bore through time as well, shortening your journey even more.

What's more, some of those physicists who believe in the idea of alternative realities have suggested a wormhole could connect you with another universe altogether.

Contrary to what you see on *Star Trek: Deep Space Nine*, nobody has found an actual wormhole yet and there are difficulties even in theory with using one as a convenient passageway. When you examine a wormhole mathematically, your calculations will show that in practical terms they're tubes leading nowhere.

The problem is a wormhole can exist for such a short time that entering it would be impossible. And if you somehow managed it, the structure would collapse before you could get anywhere. If wormholes exist, they exist for only a fraction of a second.

But that's only if you base your calculations on Newton's laws of physics or Einstein's relativity theories. Three respected scientists – the cosmologists Michael Morris, Kip Thorne and Ulvi Yurtsever – tried basing their sums on the new physics, quantum mechanics.

They came to the conclusion that some, and perhaps even many, wormholes may exist long enough to be useful.

Wormholes on Earth?

►It's probably true to say that when most scientists speculate about things like wormholes, they imagine them to exist far away in the deepest reaches of distant space. Even science-fiction writers fall into the same trap.

But if wormholes exist at all, there's no reason why they shouldn't exist on Earth ... and some evidence that they might. Take this case study, for example:

The year, 1880. The date, 23 September. The place, a farm owned by David Lang some miles outside Gallatin, Tennessee, in the USA.

It was a clear, sunny afternoon. It had been a long, hot summer and the dry spell was still far from over. Lang lived in a fairly large brick house, soundly built some years before and now covered in creepers. He farmed cattle, and some of them were grazing on the forty-acre pasture directly in front of the house. Lang was a married man. Eleven years ago, his wife had presented him with a daughter they named Sarah. Three years later, she bore him a son, George. On the morning of 23 September Lang had brought the children a new toy from Nashville – a wooden wagon with a team of wooden horses. They were playing with it in the front yard that afternoon.

Inside the house, Lang told his wife he was going to have a look at his horses to make sure they were all right. As he walked out of the house, she came after him to call out that he should hurry since she wanted him to drive her into town before the shops shut. Lang, by now on the pasture, glanced at his watch and reassured her he would be only a few minutes.

At about the time Mrs Lang was calling after her husband, a horse-drawn buggy pulled in to the lane leading to the house. It carried two men. The children stopped their play to watch. As it drew closer, it was possible to recognize the driver as a local judge, August Peck. The passenger was his brother-in-law.

Judge Peck was a good friend of the Lang family and his visits were something of an occasion. Lang spotted the buggy and waved. He began to walk back towards the house, obviously intending to greet his guests. Seconds later, he vanished. His disappearance was witnessed by Mrs Lang, the two visitors and both children.

Afterwards, under examination by the authorities, they all told the same story. One moment David Lang was walking across the pasture. The next, he was gone. It was like a stage illusion produced by a very clever conjurer. Except that it was horrifying, not entertaining.

Mrs Lang screamed. She and the children began to run towards the spot where her husband had vanished. Peck and his brother-in-law scrambled down from the buggy and did the same. They reached the spot and found nothing. No body, no remains, no scorch marks, no hole in the ground – nothing to explain the mystery of Lang's disappearance.

They began to search and kept on searching far beyond the area where Lang had disappeared. As the reality of the tragedy dawned on her, Mrs Lang began to scream. When her companions could not get her to stop, they led her gently back to the farmhouse. The experience drove her into a nervous breakdown and she remained in bed for weeks after the event.

Did a wormhole briefly open up to swallow David Lang? If so, there are a great many case histories of this type, although most of them tell of unlikely disappearances without a subsequent reappearance elsewhere, suggesting that the destination was a parallel world rather than some other part of this one.

The so-called 'Dragon's Triangle' south of Japan officially claimed 1,472 small ships (under two thousand tonnes) from 1968 to 1972. Since 1949 the official tally of major ships lost in the area is 40. In March of 1957 three planes disappeared within two weeks in this area.

Many of these losses have perfectly natural explanations but many more defy logic. Between 1949 and 1954 ten large ships vanished taking hundreds of crew members with them and leaving no trace whatsoever. In 1942 an Imperial Japanese Navy force consisting of three destroyers and two aircraft carriers disappeared.

There is no Allied report indicating these vessels were lost to enemy action.

Even more well known is the phenomena associated with the so-called Bermuda Triangle off the coast of Florida.

Here the trouble started at 2.02 p.m. on 5 December 1945, when the first of five TBM Avenger dive-bombers took off from the airstrip at Fort Lauderdale Naval Base. With World War II just over, most flights from Fort Lauderdale were routine pilot-training missions. An established pattern was followed. The planes would fly east for a distance of 160 miles over the ocean, then bear north for 40 miles. They would then turn south-west and proceed back to base. Navigation was easy. The triangle had been flown, without trouble, hundreds of times.

By 2.08 p.m. the remaining four were in the air. All five fell into formation and swung eastwards out across the ocean. Four of the planes carried a crew of three, the fifth a crew of two – pilot and navigator. Official records show all the men were experienced airmen. Weather conditions were good. There was no trouble during take-off. Radio contact was maintained.

The planes cruised out at more than 300 km/h. They completed the eastward leg successfully and made the turn towards the north without difficulty. They travelled their predetermined 40 miles and, again without difficulty, veered round to head for home. By 3.45 p.m. this routine flight should have been in sight of the naval station.

But they weren't. Instead, all five experienced navigators, aided by the most modern electronic equipment, were lost. The Flight Commander radioed his consternation back to base. They could not see land. They were not sure where they were. Ground crew anxiously scanned the sky. There was no sign of the aeroplanes.

The situation worsened. Radio messages from the planes were picked up at base and their content added to general confusion. It was obvious that the flight was in big trouble, although exactly what was the nature of the trouble no one knew – least of all the flyers themselves.

With faith in his own judgement shattered, the Flight Commander turned over his authority to another pilot.

But the new Commander did no better. The planes flew on, still out of sight of land, and no one had the least idea where they were. Someone hazarded a guess that they might be about 362 km north-east of base and this position was radioed back to the naval station. In the middle of the message, contact cut abruptly.

It was obviously a big emergency. Unlikely though it seemed, ground authorities had to conclude that all five planes had crashed simultaneously over the Atlantic. An emergency rescue operation was mounted. Spearheading it was a 13-man flying boat. It took off and headed out across the ocean. Within five minutes, radio contact with this aeroplane abruptly ceased as well.

Coast Guard aircraft flew a search pattern over the area throughout the night, but without sighting the missing aircraft. The following morning, more search aeroplanes went up, taking off from an aircraft carrier which had sailed into the vicinity. By nightfall, a further 20 aircraft carriers had joined the search. More than 300 aircraft were in the air. Twelve search parties scoured the coastline.

It was a massive rescue operation – but when, eventually, it was called off, the fate of the six missing planes was still a mystery. And the question was no longer why had they crashed, but where had they gone. For there was not the slightest trace of wreckage, no floating bodies, no oil slicks, no abandoned parachutes.

These six naval planes were not the only aircraft to vanish in the area. Towards the end of January, three years later, a British airliner with 26 on board disappeared, again without leaving wreckage or putting out any distress call.

Almost exactly a year later, a similar airliner suffered a similar fate. Altogether more than twenty planes have disappeared in this area, leaving no answer to the obvious question: Where did they go?

Historical sources show that in 1872, the riverboat *Iron Mountain* steamed out of Ticksburg *en route* to Pittsburg via Louisville and Cincinnati, towing a line of barges. The boat was 65 m long and 13 m wide. It carried 55 passengers and crew, along with a cargo of cotton and molasses. The river was busy. Only a few hours later, another steamboat discovered the barges with their tow-rope cleanly cut. There was no sign of the *Iron Mountain*, then or later. There was no sign of wreckage, no sign of bodies, no sign of survivors. In short, the riverboat had vanished without a trace. Where did it go?

There are even records of an entire Roman army that vanished without trace in Britain. It passed through many towns and villages on a march northwards, but never reached its destination. There was no battle, no bodies, no explanation.

Evidence of this sort points to the possibility that parallel universes – and wormhole gateways opening into them – may be a fact of human experience. One physicist who certainly believes so is Professor F.A. Wolf. In considering a process called quantum tunnelling, he went on record with the mind-bending statement:

If this idea is correct, much of what we now call psychic phenomena, altered states of awareness, channelling of conscious beings, spirits, ghostly apparitions, flying saucers and other unexplainable phenomena could be explained as quantum tunnelling – coming from parallel universes.

Visitors from the beyond

►Professor Wolf's theory brings together things like ghosts and flying saucers. Several UFO investigators have also wondered if there might be a connection. Among them is the veteran investigator John A. Keel who was one of the first to put forward the idea that alien contacts and alien abductions are nothing new. Both occurred just as frequently in the past as they do today, but people explained them differently.

What this means is straightforward. If you are kidnapped tonight by small humanoids who fly you miraculously to a saucer-shaped craft and transport you into unfamiliar surroundings, the chances are you'll tell everyone you were snatched by aliens when you get back.

But if the same thing happened to a boy or girl in medieval times, the chances are they'd say they were taken by the fairies.

Once you start to think of it from this viewpoint, it's obvious that history and folklore are both peppered with reports of meetings between humans and weird beings. They come from every country of the globe. In Scandinavia the creatures were described as trolls, in Ireland as the Little People, in Britain as the Fairy Folk. Native Americans had their Sky People, their Thunder Beings, their long-eared *Lacokti lanenakwe*. All were small, humanoid, able to fly and possessed 'magical' powers.

All had an unhealthy interest in the humans they met, but seldom did them very much real harm ... exactly like the 'space people' of modern UFO encounters.

Study the diagram below.

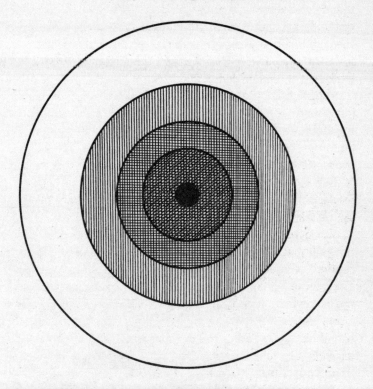

It tells you how to build a time machine.

= Section Nine =
HOW TO
BUILD A TIME
MACHINE

In the late summer of 1860, a geologist named Guiseppe Ragazzoni was collecting fossil shells at the Colle de Vento, a low hill near Castenedolo, Italy, when he discovered several human bones and the top portion of a human skull.

Professor Ragazzoni, who worked at the Technical Institute of Brescia, showed the bones to two fellow geologists. They insisted the finds must be recent burials. The bones were obviously of a modern human but their location in strata deep within the hill would have dated them as somewhere between three and four million years old – long before modern humanity evolved on the planet.

Despite the fact that the skull portion had been completely filled with fossil coral, Ragazzoni allowed himself to be persuaded and threw the bones away as scientifically worthless.

All the same, he wondered. On his own admission, he could not get out of his mind the idea of a body washed ashore by the ancient sea that once lapped the southern shores of the Alps, then covered with coral, shells and clay. Eventually he gave in to the feeling and returned to the site. To his delight, he found more bone fragments at the same depth. The theory of a recent burial was beginning to weaken.

Fifteen years later, Ragazzoni advised his friend Carlo Germani to buy a tract of land at Castenedolo. He thought Germani might make a comfortable income from it by selling the phosphate-rich clay to farmers as fertilizer. But mindful of his earlier finds, Ragazzoni asked Germani to keep an eye out for any human remains when he was excavating the clay. Germani promised to alert him if anything was discovered.

Four years later, Germani was excavating less than 18 m from the spot where Ragazzoni had made his find when he unearthed a substantial cache of human bones. Once again they were located at a depth that would have made them many millions of years old. True to his promise, Germani left the bones in place and called Ragazzoni.

Less than a month later, Germani turned up two further jaw fragments and some teeth, which he passed on to Ragazzoni, who returned personally to the site and began serious excavations of his own. They were entirely successful. The horde was now so sizeable that he realized he must be dealing with the remains of more than one individual. He also realized there was no longer any question of recent burial. All the finds were completely covered with and penetrated by clay and small fragments of coral and shells.

Early the following month came the most exciting discovery of all – a complete human skeleton that showed indications of having moved with the stratum itself, proof positive it was not a recent burial. The skull was in several pieces, but Ragazzoni had it expertly restored. It was the skull of a modern woman.

Geologists who examined the blue clay layer agreed that it belonged to the Middle Pliocene, which would make the finds between three and four million years old. The anatomist Professor Guiseppe Sergi of the University of Rome examined the remains and concluded they were of four individuals, an adult male, an adult female and two children.

Today a majority of scientists insist modern humanity is little more than 100,000 years old. In other words, the four individuals whose remains Ragazzoni found, could not possibly have lived and died in the Middle Pliocene era. But the placing of their bones show they did.

Are the scientists wrong? Did humanity evolve on our planet far earlier than they suppose? This is certainly possible. But the Ragazzoni finds are not the only mystery thrown up by the work of geologists. Over the years, evidence of human activity has been unearthed dating not simply to the Pliocene, but to much earlier eras.

These include fossilized human footprints and shoe prints more than 150 million years old, human skeletons more than 280 million years old and human artefacts – including a decorated metal vase – that are as much as 600 million years old.

The fossil record shows that humanity ultimately descended from a tiny shrew-like mammal that appeared around 75 million years ago. All these finds date from a time long before any mammal whatsoever had evolved on Earth. They could not possibly have existed in the time periods ascribed to them, yet there is firm evidence that they did. Where did they come from?

In recent years there has arisen an extraordinary theory to explain them. The theory suggests simply that many of the finds are litter left behind by *time travellers* from some future era. And the bones found are those of the travellers themselves, trapped or perhaps killed, out of their own time.

This idea seems so strange that many people are tempted to dismiss it without a second thought. But might it be worth consideration? Is time travel really possible?

Fourth dimension

➤You live in a three-dimensional world. You're aware of length, breadth and height. You're also aware of something else – time passing. But philosophers have often speculated that time is actually a fourth dimension.

According to this theory, the way you see the world is just plain wrong. If you could see things properly, you'd know yourself to be a massive worm-like creature, tapered to a baby at one end, decaying as a corpse at the other and meandering through three dimensions of space even as you extend through the fourth.

If this doesn't appeal, try looking at a time-lapse photograph of a sprint race. What you see is a series of blurring images of the athlete stretched from the starting line to the finishing tape. Any one of the images represents the three-dimensional athlete, frozen in the act of running. But the whole of the picture represents his extension in time – or at least that segment of his 'timeworm' represented by the race.

It's a philosopher's job to come up with quirky ideas, but timeworms may not be as batty as they sound. Scientists have been taking very seriously the idea of time as a fourth dimension ever since Einstein published his Special Theory of Relativity.

Einstein didn't actually say time was a fourth dimension. What he said was that there was no such thing as separate space and time. There was only one single thing called space-time.

The reason you don't see it that way is because space-time is a continuum.

Dotland

►A continuum has parts, but you can't separate them. You may remember from your geometry lessons that a line is made up of an infinite number of points. The points are bits of the line, but they're stuck together so closely that you can't take them apart. In other words, the line is a continuum.

Imagine now you live in Dotland, a country where all the inhabitants – including you – have only one dimension. You are, in other words, a living point.

If, on your travels through Dotland, you came across a line from the side (as in the diagram below), you'd have no idea it had length at all. All you'd be aware of would be a single point, just like yourself, blocking your way. You'd have to change direction before you had any inkling that the line was something more. And even then, every time you turned towards it, you'd still see nothing but a single point.

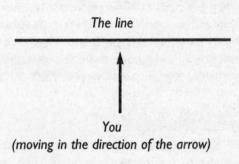

The line

You
(moving in the direction of the arrow)

If you came upon it lengthways, as shown in the second diagram, you still wouldn't see it as a line. You'd only be aware of moving from point to point on an infinite journey. However you approached it, you would never be aware of the line as a line even though (from your present three-dimensional viewpoint) you can see perfectly well that's what it *is*.

The line

Now you're coming at the line head-on from here.

It's a bit like that with space-time. Einstein reached his conclusion mathematically. Nobody actually experiences space and time as the same thing. However you experience it, you still think of space as space and time as time.

You're in good company. Sir Isaac Newton, the father of physics, thought there were three dimensions of space and everything in them moved forward through one dimension of time. Everybody else accepted that for centuries. But the reality of Special Relativity is that from a four-dimensional viewpoint everything past, present and future already exists as a single fabric. That isn't the way you experience it any more than the one-dimensional being experiences the line as a line, but that's the way it is.

The Minowski equations

▶Einstein once remarked he wasn't very good at maths. Fortunately, he had a teacher named Herman Minowski who was prepared to do the hard work for him. Three years after Einstein published the first of his two theories of relativity, Minowski had calculated its mathematical implications.

Those calculations were poetry. They showed mathematically the whole of your past and the whole of your future must meet at a single point, the eternal *now* of space-time. And the meeting point has a specific location. It can never be found other than at the precise position of you. All of your past, all of your future converges mathematically at the instant you read these words on the exact spot where you read them.

You can change your position in space quite easily. You've probably done it a thousand times today. Each time you did, the whole forwards/backwards meeting point of your future and your past moved with you, leaving the whole space/time continuum intact.

But the real question is, can you change your position in time?

Time travel

►Einstein thought you could and even showed how in his famous Twins Paradox.

The Twins Paradox wasn't meant to be about time travel, but about what happens when things get close to the speed of light. Relativity theory shows that when you move, time runs slower than when you're standing still. The difference is too small to measure when you're on a bus, and even on the fastest jet plane you need a super-accurate atomic clock to record it. But as you get up near light speed (299,330 km per second) time slows down a lot.[8]

Against this background, Einstein asked his colleagues to consider a variation of the following situation:

You have a pair of twins who are now, say, 17 years old. One of them climbs on board a super-fast spaceship to boldly go where no twin has gone before. The other one stays home to form a pop group.

The space-faring twin stays away for five years, according to the clocks on his ship. When he gets back to Earth, he's 22 years old. But the ship was racing close to the speed of light so that time inside it was running seven times more slowly than it did on Earth. That means his twin is now 52 years old and has dropped pop music in favour of Beethoven.

Not only is the Earth twin older, but everything else on Earth has moved ahead 30 years when measured against the calendar inside the ship. So from the point of view of the space twin, he's travelled 30 years into the future.

This is time travel of a sort. But shifting in time by speeding round the cosmos is strictly a one-way trip. You can zip into the future, but there's no way you can zip into the past.

Time machine

➤The scientific establishment held real two-way time travel to be a myth until 1996 when the world's most famous (and arguably smartest) physicist, Professor Stephen Hawking of Cambridge University, announced he'd changed his mind. From thinking it was quite impossible, he now thought it might be possible at least in theory, although he didn't really believe he'd get a round-trip ticket in his lifetime.

But as long ago as the 1970s, the possibility of real time travel was widely accepted by a more maverick element of North American physicists. On the basis of four-dimensional Einsteinian space-time, they couldn't really see what there was to stop you. All you needed was a large enough mass, which the relativity equations showed must warp space-time.

One of the mavericks, physicist Frank Tipler, went so far as publishing plans for the world's first time machine. As long ago as 1974, his time-travel ideas appeared in *Physical Review*, a perfectly respectable scientific journal. They never got wider publicity, possibly because he published them under the bewildering title 'Rotating Cylinders and the Possibility of Global Causality Violation'.

It turned out that a 'global causality violation' was a path that winds through space and turns around in time. It is something that will not only allow you to travel through time, to the future or the past, but will also take you back to the time you started. You could have a wonderful adventure for as long as you wanted, but to the outside world you wouldn't have gone anywhere because you got back at the exact instant you left.

A small band of physicists interested in time travel thought it might be possible to create a path like this by spinning some ultra-dense matter. They call the path a closed timelike line.

The calculations show there are closed timelike lines associated with rotating black holes – you have to go through black holes twice to complete the loop. They're also associated with wormholes and here again you have to squeeze through two wormholes on your closed timelike line to come out in the same universe you left. You can see Tipler's idea of creating a path like this under controlled conditions seemed a lot safer than using the natural paths created by black holes or wormholes.

Tipler summed up his scheme in a single sentence: 'General Relativity suggests that if we construct a sufficiently large rotating cylinder, we create a time machine.'

Time travel in theory

➤The theory was straightforward enough. If it's big enough and dense enough and spinning fast enough, it warps space-time. Read that sentence again. It doesn't warp space, it warps *space-time*. It distorts the fabric so that instead of following its old familiar path from past to future, time actually swings backwards and forwards like the pendulum of a clock. Catch it on one swing and you're moving forward in time. Catch it on another and you're travelling backwards.

The swings form zones. If you're very careful, you might be able to fly into a backward-running time zone without getting yourself ripped to pieces by the forces of gravity. Here's a diagram of a Tipler cylinder with its associated zones, based on the one that appears in Fred Alan Wolf's book *Parallel Universes*. It's not to scale and you're looking at it end-on.

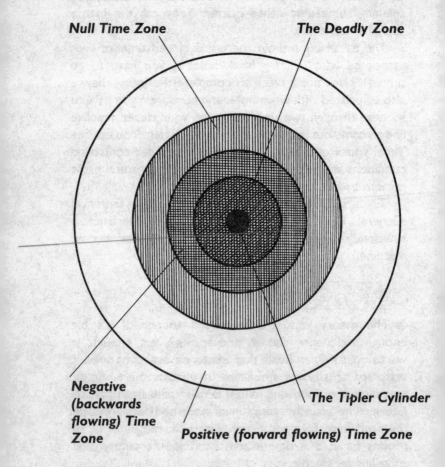

Null Time Zone

The Deadly Zone

Negative (backwards flowing) Time Zone

The Tipler Cylinder

Positive (forward flowing) Time Zone

How do you build a thing like that? The answer is, not easily.

Building a time machine

➤The cylinder itself is the solid black circle in the middle. It's gigantic, it's dense and it's spinning. Your biggest problem is what to make it from. You can't just forge a giant cylinder in steel, hew it from wood, carve it in stone or extrude it from plastic. If you used any of these materials, the cylinder would be so large it would fill the entire galaxy.

What you need is some sort of super-dense material. This needs to have a huge mass, but take up very little room. We've already talked about that sort of material. You could mine it on a neutron star. Except to build a working cylinder, you wouldn't just need material mined from a neutron star, you'd need the whole star. In fact, you'd need about a hundred.

Dr Wolf has worked out the finer details. A working Tipler cylinder would have to be about 40 kilometres across and 4,000 kilometres long. The design is a trade-off. You need something that generates a reverse time zone far enough away from its spinning surface to allow you to enter the zone without being crushed by gravity. To do that, you need a very long cylinder. A hundred neutron stars sounds a lot, but while they have immense mass, as stars go they're very small.

Tipler's plans call not only for a cylinder, but a spinning cylinder. Fortunately most neutron stars are already spinning on their own axes. Wolf calculates that the cylinder will need a rotation of around 10,000 revs per second which, fortunately, falls within the range of a typical neutron star. By synchronizing the 10,000 revolution spins of a hundred neutron stars herded together in a line, you have a cylinder which, at its surface, is spinning at about three-quarters the speed of light. This does very nicely to produce the zones at a distance far enough from the cylinder for you to be able to use them.

Obviously you won't build this time machine on Earth. Four thousand kilometres is about the width of the United States, but even if you persuaded the President to allow it, the gravitational mass would destroy the whole planet. So the Tipler cylinder will have to be constructed somewhere in space, preferably an area of space where there is little or no natural gravitational interference. That takes it way outside the solar system.

Once it's in place and spinning, the Tipler cylinder generates a 20-kilometre-wide zone where the fabric of space-time is grossly distorted. You'll see this on the diagram as the 'Deadly Zone'. Keep well away from that one. The conditions there wouldn't just kill you – they'd destroy you utterly and there's no known way you could protect yourself. But maybe the Deadly Zone isn't as dangerous as it sounds, since there's a real chance you couldn't get inside it if you tried – many physicists are convinced you'd be pushed back by the very nature of space-time at its outer boundary.

Surrounding the Deadly Zone is the zone of time reversal. This is the area of space where time runs backwards. Get yourself in there and you're a time traveller.

The time travel zone is surrounded by a null time zone, a sort of interface between negative and positive time. In the null time zone, time stands still.

Finally, you have a positive time zone – one, that is, where time runs in the familiar past-to-future direction.

Once these zones are created, the time machine is ready to use. Have your ship's computer plot a course that lets you approach the cylinder end-on. If you approach at an angle to the axis of spin you won't be able to reach the zone you need. But since the zones are rings, not spheres, you can come at them sideways.

As your ship approaches, you'll notice that the zones are visible. The Deadly Zone actually glows quite prettily, as matter-antimatter annihilations generate violet photons. Aim for the second zone, the time travel zone, keeping carefully parallel to the axis of the cylinder.

As you get closer, you'll start to feel heavy. Closer still and the weight becomes crushing. You're experiencing the massive gravity produced by the spinning cylinder, but if Fred Wolf has done his sums right it will be uncomfortable, but it won't get bad enough to kill you. Hang in there, breathe deeply and tell yourself it's all going to be worth it yesterday. Because when your ship enters the zone, you're no longer flying through space.

You've switched to the fourth-dimensional axis and are flying through time.

The time gate

▶It's clear that building a Tipler cylinder is far beyond the technology available today. But it would be unreasonable to insist that this will always be the case. Although we've no more idea how to move neutron stars than a caveman had of how to build a jet aeroplane, it's reasonable to believe that given a few hundred or a few thousand years, we might figure out the technical problems involved.

And that brings up a fascinating possibility. Because if a Tipler cylinder is ever built – in a hundred years' time, or ten thousand years' time, or a billion years' time – by human beings or any other intelligent race within the galaxy, then the time gate that it opens must stretch right through to the present day. If a Tipler cylinder exists in AD 1 billion, then it automatically exists today, last week and in the days when dinosaurs roamed the Earth.

This means if you can build a spaceship that will take you beyond the solar system (something that *isn't* too far beyond current technology), then you might, just might, find your way towards the violet light that beckons you towards a time gate that's open right now, at this minute.

If, as the evidence suggests, 'aliens' have been making contact with humanity for generations, is it possible they're using such a time gate? In some ways, the idea makes more sense than the theory that these visitors have flown in from a distant star. It would, for example, explain why so many of them are humanoid in shape and able to breathe our air. It would also explain their long-term interest in humanity – the same interest that prompts us to study history.

But is it really likely that the evidence of 'alien contact' can best be explained as contact with a future humanity so far along the evolutionary path that they differ from us as we differ from Neanderthals? There is one curious fact that might suggest it is.

Although calculations show a Tipler cylinder could generate usable zones, the gravity involved would still place considerable strain on a time traveller. In order to minimize the effect, Fred Alan Wolf suggests the only logical shape for a time ship would be a flattened disc.

In other words, a flying saucer.

Here's a message from somewhere:

'Micma Goho Mad Zir Comselha Zien Biah
Os Londoh Norz Chis Othil Gigipah Vnd-L
Chis ta Pu-Im Q Mospleh Teloch'

**What's the betting it's written in the language of
an alien contact?**

167

Section Ten

MESSAGES FROM BEYOND

The year is 1554. Queen Mary is on the throne of England. The country has been forced to follow the Roman Catholic faith and rebellion is in the air.

At Woodstock, near London, Mary's half-sister, the Princess Elizabeth, is under house arrest. Although outwardly a Catholic, she knows she is the focus of many plots to restore Protestantism. She awaits daily the summons back to the Tower of London for beheading like her mother.

One day she receives a strange visitor. Although only 27 years old, John Dee is the best-known scholar in the country. He has already studied and lectured extensively throughout Europe and was so highly thought of when he returned to England just three years ago that the government granted him a pension.

Dee is interested in mathematics, alchemy, history and geometry. But it is none of these things that has brought him to Woodstock. His most abiding fascination is astrology and despite the danger involved he wants to tell Elizabeth what her horoscope predicts. The princess listens open-mouthed...

What the stars foretold

➤It's a matter of historical record that, at a time when few people in the country would have given her much chance of surviving the year, Dr John Dee told the young Princess Elizabeth that not only would she live, but she was destined to become the Queen of England.

If word of this prediction had leaked out, there is no doubt at all he would have been executed. As it was, he became briefly Court Astrologer to Queen Mary, but was jailed soon after for practising magic. Astrology, which included astronomy, was a respected and respectable art, taught in the universities. Magic was heresy and often led to burning at the stake.

But Dee didn't burn. His friends at Court persuaded the authorities he was innocent and engineered his release from jail in 1555. Soon, he found himself with a new job. He was recruited as an Admiralty spy and issued with the code number 007.

When, against all odds, Elizabeth came to the throne in 1558, she didn't forget his prediction. Dee was asked to calculate a propitious day for her coronation and later given back his old job as Court Astrologer. His own future seemed assured. He was so close to the Queen that he used to give her lessons in the mystical interpretation of his writings. He had his stipend as a spy and made more trips to Europe financed by his master Francis Walsingham. His knowledge of maps and navigation enabled him to take up a third career by advising sailors who had just begun to explore the New World of the Americas.

Dark side

▶But there was a darker side to John Dee. The early accusations of sorcery were well founded. The scholarly scientist had an abiding interest in magic. In 1582, he began a series of experiments in the conjuring of spirits.

Dee's contemporary, William Shakespeare, wrote a play about magic, *The Tempest*. In it, Prospero boasts, 'I can call spirits from the vasty deep!' But another, less credulous, character responds, 'Aye, but do they come when you do call for them?'

Dee's spirits didn't come either. He'd tried, like Prospero, to call them, but none appeared. In a more cynical age, this might have been taken as evidence that spirits didn't exist (or if they did, they had no interest in communicating with humans). Dee, however, concluded they were there but he wasn't able to see them.

His solution was to hire (for £50 a year) the services of a psychic. His choice fell on a scoundrel of Irish extraction named Edward Kelley. Kelley had a criminal record. He wore a skullcap pulled well down over his head to hide the fact his ears were missing – they'd been cropped for counterfeiting coins. He boasted he knew the secret of making gold out of lead and other metals, but never seemed to have two pennies to rub together. Despite all this, Dee trusted him.

Although the work they did together was secret, Dee's diaries have survived so we know exactly what went on. Kelley would stare into a 'shewstone' – a sort of crystal ball – while Dee, the magician, would call on the spirits. This short extract from Dee's record tells the story:

'Suddenly there seemed to come out of my Oratory a *Spirituall creature*, like a pretty *girle* of 7 or 9 yeares of age, attired on her head with her hair rowled up before and hanging down very long behind, with a gown of Sey ... and seemed to go in and out behind my books ... and as she should ever go between them, the books seemed to give place sufficiently ...'

Dee asked, 'Whose maiden are you?'

The girl promptly came back with, 'Whose man are you?'

Not at all taken aback by the question, Dee told her, 'I am a servant of God both by my bound duty and also (I hope) by his Adoption.'

At which the spirit remarked, 'Am not I a fine Maiden? Give me leave to play in your house, my Mother told me she would come and dwell here.'

Angelic dictation

►Although it's not obvious from his diary, Dee was communicating with the spirit second-hand. Kelley looked in the crystal then reported what was happening and what the girl was saying.

You wouldn't be the first to wonder why an intelligent man like Dee spent so much of his time listening to and writing down nonsense. But he kept at it month after month and by June 1583, the experiments took a weird turn. Instead of sweet little girl spirits, the two men found themselves in contact with an impatient angel named Ave.

Under instruction from the angel, Dee and Kelley made up more than a hundred large squares of card, each measuring more than a metre square. On these cards they drew a grid with a particular pattern of letters. During their seances, Dee placed these huge cards on a writing table in front of him, while Kelley sat across the room staring into the crystal shewstone.

Over a series of weeks, Ave (speaking through Kelley) dictated a series of messages in an unknown language. The process of transcribing the messages was bizarre. Kelley would report sight of the angel in the shewstone where he could also see the angel's own copies of the cards. Using a wand, the angel would then point to certain letters on the cards and Kelley would call them out. Dee would then locate the letter in the same position in his tablet and write it down. In this way, each message was built up backwards. It was supposed to be reversed in order to read it the right way around.

The odd method of dictation – letter by letter and backwards – was explained by the fact that the messages were so powerful even writing them down in the normal way might stir up powerful energies. Dee was kept hard at work by the promise that the messages had great magical power.

The quote at the beginning of this chapter – 'Micma Goho Mad Zir Comselha Zien Biah Os Londoh Norz Chis Othll Gigipah Vnd L Chis ta Pu-Im Q Mospleh Teloch ...' – is a brief example of the sort of message that came through. There is a translation into English – about 'twelve kingdoms' and 'seats of living breath' – but it's only slightly less obscure than the original.

Where did the messages come from?

►Where did these weird messages come from? The obvious answer is that Kelley made them up. He had to do something to keep Dee happy and earn his £50 a year.

But there's a problem with this explanation. Linguists who've examined the messages say they're not gibberish, not a code and not a cipher. They're an actual language, internally consistent and with its own syntax.

It's not impossible that someone could have invented this language. Artificial languages have certainly been created – Esperanto is a modern example. But outside the notebooks of John Dee, there is no record of it. If it was developed by some bright Elizabethan scholar one wonders why he never seems to have written it down or tried to exploit it for money or even told anyone about it.

Nor is it impossible – although it seems far less likely – that Kelley invented it himself. But having developed a whole new language, Kelley would then have had to memorize 48 lengthy messages in it. Dee was naïve, but not stupid. He watched his medium too carefully for Kelley to have used any form of prompt card in the seances. Not only that, but Kelley would have had to memorize the messages so well that he could dictate them backwards.

Given Kelley's dislike of hard work it would be easier to believe he really did talk to angels.

If so, he would not have been the first. Throughout history, and in all probability throughout prehistory as well, there have been people who believed they heard the voices of spirits, angels, even sometimes gods.

In modern times, while true believers continue to exist, the best scientific opinion was that anyone who got messages from (usually) invisible entities was either mad or listening to projections of their own unconscious.

But then, in the early 1960s, something happened to change all that.

Electronic voices

➤What happened was that a Swedish film producer named Friedrich Jürgenson went out into the woods to record birdsong. Jürgenson was a keen amateur bird watcher who had recorded birdsong often before. But on this occasion, as he played back his tape, he heard a faint, strange noise like someone calling his name.

He adjusted the volume and discovered that a voice was definitely there. He thought it was the voice of his mother. But his mother had been dead for years. It seemed he was listening to the world's first electronic ghost.

Jürgenson produced many more mysterious recordings and in 1964 brought out a book about them called *Voices from Space*. Among those who read it was a Latvian psychiatrist, Dr Konstantin Raudive. He was so impressed that, in April 1965, he contacted Jürgenson and asked for a demonstration. Jürgenson agreed.

Dr Raudive and his colleague, Dr Zenta Maurina, found it difficult to make out the voices at first. They were faint and spoke very quickly with a peculiar rhythm. But as the tapes were replayed over and over, their ears gradually attuned.

At first they had no way of knowing if the voices were what Jürgenson claimed them to be. It was entirely possible they had been made in the usual way with a microphone. But then Jürgenson agreed to make a brand-new recording on the spot. He set up his machine, let it run for a while, then played back the tape. There were voices on it that couldn't have come from anybody in the room.

They didn't seem to be just random noise either. One of them actually answered Dr Maurina when she remarked that people seemed to have a happy, carefree existence in the Afterlife.

'*Nonsense!*' exclaimed the weird recorded voice.

Other explanations

➤Although Jürgenson was certain he had been recording ghosts, Dr Raudive wasn't so sure. He thought the voices could be freak radio transmissions and even wondered if his, or Jürgenson's, unconscious mind might somehow have managed to leave impressions on the tape. He decided to join Jürgenson to carry out research. By 10 June 1965, he had made his first good quality electronic voice recording.

It was a strange one. First there was a voice calling 'Friedrich, Friedrich.' Then a woman's voice said softly, 'Heute pa nakti. Kennt ihr Margaret, Konstantin?' After a brief pause, the same voice sang, 'Vi tálu! Runá!' Finally a different female voice said, 'Va à dormir, Margaret!'

This may not make a lot of sense to you, even if you are good at languages. The problem is it's not one language, but a mixture, combining words in German, Latvian, French and, possibly, English.

Fortunately, Dr Raudive was an exceptional linguist,

well able to separate out the various elements of the message. Translated, it read: 'Fredrick, Fredrick! Tonight. Do you know Margaret, Konstantin? We are far away! Speak! Go to sleep, Margaret.'

This hit Dr Raudive like a thunderbolt. A friend of his named Margaret had recently died and he was convinced the message referred to her. He decided to see if he could make recordings of this type without Jürgenson.

It took him three months before a taped voice answered one of his own spoken observations with the words, 'Pareizi tá büs!' – Latvian for 'That's right!'

This was the first of a series of recordings that numbered more than 30,000 by the time of Dr Raudive's death.

At first he picked up voices of dead relatives and friends. Then more famous people started to communicate. Raudive found he had recorded the author Tolstoy, who wrote *War and Peace*, the great psychiatrist Carl Jung, Stalin, Hitler, Mussolini and even Winston Churchill. The interesting thing was that while Tolstoy and Stalin both spoke Russian, almost all the rest of Dr Raudive's voices came through in a mixture of languages, like the one quoted earlier.

Why this should be so, nobody was quite sure, although it seems to have had something to do with the enormous number of languages Dr Raudive himself spoke fluently. Certainly when other people started to record the voices, multilingual messages were quite unusual.

But other people *could* persuade the voices to come through quite easily. When news of the voices reached Ireland, for example, a television researcher named Pan Collins managed to get a distinctive voice recording on her very first attempt.

Real voices

►If you listen long enough to white noise, you'll start to hear the faint echo of distant voices within it. This is because your brain gets bored and starts to imagine sounds that just aren't there. But the Raudive/Jürgenson voices aren't like that. Electronics experts soon determined they leave actual traces on the tape.

The next thing was to rule out fraud or things like freak radio transmissions. Engineers set up experiment after experiment, using more and more sophisticated equipment screened against all possible interference. The voices still came through.

Make your own recordings

►There are three ways of producing electronic voice recordings, two of them very simple indeed. All you need is patience and some fairly basic equipment. The three methods are as follows:

The Diode Method
This method gives the clearest voices, but requires the most equipment. To try it, you will need a radio, a short aerial (somewhere between 6 and 10 cm), a recorder and a part called a diode.

Since almost any radio and recorder can be used, the only thing likely to cause difficulty is the diode, which you'll have to buy at a radio or electronics shop. Fortunately, it is a simple piece of equipment and shouldn't be expensive.

You attach the aerial to the diode and the diode to the radio. Turn on the medium waveband and tune your set to what is technically known as an inter-frequency – anywhere on the waveband where no station is broadcasting. What you are looking for is 'white noise', a constant hiss of static.

Set your recorder to record from the radio, either via a microphone or, better, using a cable input. Let your recorder run for at least half an hour or longer. If you use an open microphone to record, make sure there are no noises in the room or outside that the mike can pick up.

This method is likely to give you the best results unless you live close to a strong radio transmitter, which can cause interference that's difficult to block.

The Radio Method

This is almost identical to the last method except that it doesn't use a diode.

Join your radio to your tape recorder exactly as you would if you were planning to record a programme. As before, find a spot on the medium waveband between two stations where background noise is as little as possible.

Alternatively, you can get up early in the morning and find a carrier wave – the irritating sound stations beam out on their particular frequency before they actually start to broadcast. Once you get your carrier wave, start recording.

The Microphone Method.

This is the simplest method of all, but it can still provide very satisfactory results.

You simply set up your recorder and microphone in the usual way in an empty, quiet room and record the silence for half an hour or so.

Listening in

➤Setting up to record the voices isn't all that difficult. The difficulty arises when you play back the tape. Until you're very well used to them, the voices are amazingly difficult to hear. Often you'll have to play an apparently blank tape over and over before your ear suddenly tunes in and catches something.

Even then, it may take several more playbacks before you begin to make out words. It gets easier with practice, but you need a lot of patience at the start.

What are the voices?

►But even when you start to hear them, the question still arises: what, exactly, are you listening to?

There seems little doubt that the electronic voices discovered by Jürgenson and Raudive are the same voices psychics, shamans and mediums have been hearing through the centuries. They turn up in much the same circumstances. They talk the same sort of nonsense. And they are often thought to be the spirits of the dead.

But are they?

Raudive heard the name *Margaret* and assumed the reference was to his dead friend. But Margaret is a common enough name. Perhaps the reference was to somebody else. A great many of the electronic messages are like that. The voices themselves make no claims. It's the people listening who *assume* they're ghosts.

Even Raudive's collection of famous names – Stalin, Hitler, Churchill and the rest – may not be what they seem. Certainly their style of conversation is a far cry from the way they sounded in life.

Then there is the problem of the multilingual messages. These seem to be the trademark of Dr Raudive, who was himself fluent in many languages, as if he somehow influenced the content. If he had been a medium sitting in a seance, we might have been tempted to decide the voices were the product of his unconscious mind.

Yet the bottom line remains: the voices, for all their faults and limitations, are real. Listen carefully and you can hear them on the Raudive tapes, and even make tapes of your own. Electronic analysis shows the same blips on the magnetic surface of the tape that would occur if you'd recorded your own speech with a microphone.

If this is some sort of electronic freak, some accident of the magnetic tape, experts have so far failed to find it. Despite test after test, it still seems as though something seems to be trying to make contact.

EPILOGUE

It's difficult to know what to make of any of this. Put all the evidence together and the picture that emerges is fascinating, disturbing, exciting, but very far from clear.

First, you have the historical evidence. People in all ages, from every country of the globe, have claimed to have seen, met, touched, talked to strange beings with what appeared to be 'supernatural' or 'magical' powers. Sometimes these creatures carried off their human contacts to unfamiliar places – the 'underworld' or 'fairyland' – where strange effects seem to be the norm.

Such trips often distort time. Over and over, folklore tells how the hero spends an hour in fairyland only to find on his return that a century or more has passed on Earth. Or the hero lives a lifetime in fairyland, only to discover no time has passed at all when he returns.

Side by side with these curious encounters are the even more widespread reports of messages from the beyond. Messages from 'angels' like the one who contacted Dr Dee. Messages from 'dead relatives' speaking through Spiritualist mediums. Messages from 'spirits' speaking to shamans. Messages from the 'gods' of Voodoo. Messages from African 'ancestors'. Messages from medieval 'demons'.

This ancient pattern, so often thought of as superstition, is repeated in our own day. Mediums still sit in seances. Messages impress themselves on recording tape. Lights appear in the sky. Strange beings waylay decent people like the Hills at night. But now the way we interpret the contact has changed. Instead of gods, demons, fairies or the host of supernatural beings that have appeared down the ages, we think of the creatures as 'aliens' in 'spaceships' or 'time ships' or 'inter-dimensional vehicles'. Their 'magic' is now put down to high technology.

Where do these contacts come from?

There is still a widespread school of thought that insists alien encounters are a product of the imagination. This theory says, in short, that people who see fairies or flying saucers are either lying or hallucinating. If this is so, then the number of liars and lunatics on the planet has increased alarmingly in recent years. The pollsters calculate the number of supposed alien contacts in America may now run to several millions – and that is just one country. Heaven alone knows what the figure must be worldwide.

It is, of course, no argument against lunacy to say that the asylums are full – rather the reverse. It may be that the pressures of life generate a well-established psychological response in more and more people these days. Certainly what was what Dr Jung thought when he published his *Flying Saucers: A Modern Myth of Things Seen in the Sky*.

The term 'myth' in Jung's title reflects the basic theory of his book. Jung believed that humanity constructed 'great stories' (myths) to try to explain the world and often projected the contents of these stories outwards into observations of reality. In this way, people of old sensed spirits in trees, stones, rivers, desert sands. They met with fairies, ghosts and demons. They listened to ancestral voices.

Today, Jung argued, the old religious myths and widespread superstitions have lost much of their power, but the need for them remains. Since humanity could not live without a sense of meaning, it reacted to the loss of its old myths by inventing new ones. These were the ancient stories of salvation from heaven in a new guise. We no longer believe in gods, but we can believe in visitors from space.

It's easy to see how neatly Jung's argument fits not only the flying saucers discussed at considerable length in his book, but other phenomena as well, including the voices heard by mediums and the messages left on Raudive's tapes.

But even Jung admitted a problem with his theory. The problem, simply stated, was that many UFOs appeared on radar. (And we might add that Raudive's messages really do appear on tape.) They are not simply imagination.

But if it's not imagination, what then? Dr Drake and his colleagues still scan the skies for radio messages from outer space. The good doctor expects to hear from ET any day, but so far there's been nothing. Have the aliens abandoned conventional technology in favour of telepathy? There are New Age channellers who are convinced they are in touch with intelligences from distant galaxies.

Yet if the mental messages originate in outer space, why do so many of them claim to be religious figures like angels or the spirits of the dead? And what of the idea that we might sometimes meet up with visitors from our own future? Perhaps there is more than one source of alien contact and this has confused the picture even further.

In recent years, scientists with no interest whatsoever in alien contact have discovered evidence for other dimensions of reality.

Although put in different terms at different times, the idea of other dimensions of reality is very old. For much of human history these alien dimensions have been viewed in a mythic or religious light. Only in the last century has the mathematics of physics shown such weird dimensions must actually exist. The question is, are they inhabited?

Or is this, like so many other explanations, far too simple? If we return for a moment to Jung and his idea that human belief creates the great mythic patterns evident in UFOs, alien abductions and all the other forms of 'contact' we have been examining, is it possible that the human mind could actually alter reality? Are UFOs and Raudive voices hallucinations that have taken *physical* form?

The questions seem endless. You are the only one who can decide on the answers.

NOTES

1. Quoted from *The McDaniel Report*.

2. Although at time of writing we haven't even done that yet.

3. Quoted from the introduction of *Chariot of the Gods?* Souvenir Press, London 1969. Bantam Books, New York, 1971.

4. *Flying Saucers Have Landed* by Desmond Leslie and George Adamski, Neville Spearman, London, 1970.

5. Ibid.

6. Ibid.

7. Quoted from *From Outer Space to You*, by Howard Menger. Saucerian Publications, 1959.

8. When you reach the speed of light it stops altogether.

TALKING POINT

Talking Point tackles the kind of issues that affect all of us and asks teenagers what they *really* think.

Available now:
The Internet. Herbie Brennan
How to get on the Net, what you'll find when you get there, and how the Net could change the future.

Designer Genes. Phil Gates
From Dolly the sheep to pig heart transplants, what is genetic engineering really all about, and what are the implications?

Look out for:
Animals Behind Bars. Sylvia Funston
Are free-range hens *really* happy? Does science still torture animals? And if we care so much, why aren't we all vegan?

Global Warming. Paul Simons
Are temperatures really rising, and if so, why? Are we all in danger of ruining our ecosystem ... for ever?